THE GOLDEN BOOK OF FAVORITE SONGS

Revised and Enlarged

A Treasury of the Best Songs of Our People

(202 songs, 192 of which are with music)

Compiled and edited by

John W. Beattie
Dean, School of Music
Northwestern University

William Breach
Supervisor of Music
Buffalo, New York

Mabelle Glenn
Director of Public School Music
Kansas City, Missouri

Walter J. Goodell
Composer and Harmonist
Chicago, Illinois

Edgar B. Gordon
Bureau of Extension, University of Wisconsin
Madison, Wisconsin

Norman H. Hall
Executive Secretary, National Week of Song
Chicago, Illinois

Ernest G. Hesser
Chairman, Department of Music Education
New York University

E. Jane Wisenall
Former Teacher of Music, Woodward High School
Cincinnati, Ohio

(Twentieth Edition—Revised)

HALL & McCREARY COMPANY
CHICAGO

Responsive Readings

LEADER: *Blessed is the nation whose God is the Lord,*
And the people whom he hath chosen for his own inheritance.

ASSEMBLY: Righteousness exalteth a nation; but sin is a reproach to any people.

LEADER: *When the righteous are in authority the people rejoice; but when the wicked beareth rule, the people mourn.*
If thou hearken diligently unto the voice of the Lord thy God,
The Lord thy God will set thee on high above all nations of the earth.

Psalms

UNISON: We hold these truths to be self-evident:
That all men are created equal;
That they are endowed by their Creator with certain inalienable rights;
That among these are life, liberty, and the pursuit of happiness;
That to secure these rights, governments are instituted among men, deriving their just powers from the consent of the governed.

Thomas Jefferson

Lincoln's Gettysburg Address

LEADER: *Fourscore and seven years ago our fathers brought forth on this continent a new nation, conceived in liberty, and dedicated to the proposition that all men are created equal.*

ASSEMBLY: Now we are engaged in a great civil war, testing whether that nation, or any nation so conceived and so dedicated, can long endure.

LEADER: *We are met on a great battle-field of that war. We have come to dedicate a portion of that field as a final resting-place for those who here gave their lives that that nation might live.*

ASSEMBLY: It is altogether fitting and proper that we should do this. But, in a larger sense we cannot dedicate—we cannot consecrate—we cannot hallow—this ground.

LEADER: *The brave men, living and dead, who struggled here, have consecrated it far above our poor power to add or detract.*

ASSEMBLY: The world will little note nor long remember what we say here, but it can never forget what they did here.

LEADER: *It is for us, the living, rather, to be dedicated here to the unfinished work which they who fought here have thus far so nobly advanced.*

ASSEMBLY: It is rather for us to be here dedicated to the great task remaining before us—that from these honored dead we take increased devotion to that cause for which they gave the last full measure of devotion;

That we here highly resolve that these dead shall not have died in vain; that this nation, under God, shall have a new birth of freedom; and that the government of the people, by the people, for the people, shall not perish from the earth.

Abraham Lincoln

LEADER: *God hath made of one blood all nations of men, and we are his children,—brothers and sisters all.*

ASSEMBLY: We are citizens of these United States, and we believe our Flag stands for self-sacrifice for the good of all the people. We want, therefore, to be true citizens of our great country, and will show our love for her by our works.

LEADER: *Our country does not ask us to die for her welfare; she asks us to live for her, and so to live and so to act that her government may be pure, her officers honest, and every corner of her territory shall be a place fit to grow the best men and women, who shall rule over her.*

Mary McDowell

UNISON: The Flag means universal education—light for every mind, knowledge for every child. We must have but one flag. We must also have but one language. This must be the language of the Declaration of Independence.

Woodrow Wilson

Pledge To The Flag

I pledge allegiance to the Flag of the United States of America and to the Republic for which it stands, One Nation indivisible, with liberty and justice for all.

America

(My Country, 'Tis of Thee)

America was written by Rev. Samuel F. Smith, a Baptist minister, who was born in Boston, October 21, 1808, and died November 16, 1895.

One of Dr. Smith's friends was Lowell Mason, the eminent musician. A friend had given Mr. Mason a lot of German music books. Being unable to read German the musician took the books to Dr. Smith and asked him to translate some of the songs for him.

Dr. Smith says: "Turning over the leaves of the book one gloomy day in February, 1832, I came across the air, 'God save the King.' I liked the music. I glanced at the German words at the foot of the page. Under the inspiration of the moment I went to work and in half an hour 'America' was the result. It was written on a scrap of paper I picked up from the table and the hymn of today is substantially as it was written that day."

The hymn was first sung at a children's Fourth of July celebration in Park Street Church, Boston. It did not have great popularity until the Civil War. Since then it has become the best known and most frequently sung of any of our national songs. The origin of the music is uncertain. But one writer aptly says: "There certainly must be something more than ordinarily inspiring in an air which has struck the popular heart of two of the great nations of the earth."

SAMUEL FRANCIS SMITH — HENRY CAREY (?)

With a moderately quick motion

1. My country, 'tis of thee, Sweet land of lib-er-ty, Of thee I sing. Land where my
2. My na-tive coun-try, thee, Land of the no-ble free, Thy name I love. I love thy
3. Let mu-sic swell the breeze, And ring from all the trees Sweet freedom's song. Let mortal
4. Our fathers' God, to Thee, Author of lib-er-ty, To Thee we sing. Long may our

fa-thers died! Land of the Pil-grim's pride! From ev-'ry mountain side, Let freedom ring!
rocks and rills, Thy woods and templed hills; My heart with rapture thrills Like that a-bove.
tongues awake; Let all that breathe partake; Let rocks their silence break, The sound prolong.
land be bright With freedom's ho-ly light; Protect us by Thy might, Great God, our King!

God Bless Our Native Land

(Tune — America)

1. God bless our native land,
Firm may she ever stand
Through storm and night!
When the wild tempests rave,
Ruler of wind and wave,
Do thou our country save,
By thy great might!

2. For her our prayers shall rise,
To God above the skies,
On him we wait;
Thou who art ever nigh,
Guarding with watchful eye,
To Thee aloud we cry,
God save the state!

CHARLES T. BROOKS AND JOHN S. DWIGHT

The American's Creed

"I believe in the United States of America as a Government of the people, by the people, for the people; whose just powers are derived from the consent of the governed; a democracy in a republic; a sovereign Nation of many sovereign States; a perfect union, one and inseparable; established upon those principles of freedom, equality, justice, and humanity for which American patriots sacrificed their lives and fortunes.

"I therefore believe it is my duty to my country to love it; to support its Constitution; to obey its laws; to respect its flag, and to defend it against all enemies." — William Tyler Page.

The Star-Spangled Banner

The "Star-Spangled Banner" was composed under the following circumstances:
It was on the evening of September 13, 1814, during the War of 1812, that a British fleet was anchored in Chesapeake Bay. A Dr. Beanes, an old resident of Upper Marlborough, Maryland, had been captured by the British and sent as a prisoner to Admiral Cochrane's flagship.

Francis Scott Key, a young lawyer of Baltimore, hearing of the misfortune of Dr. Beanes, who was his personal friend, hastened to the British commander to endeaver to have his friend released. The enemy was about to attack Fort McHenry, so refused to allow Mr. Key and Dr. Beanes to return until after the fort was captured.

All through the night of September 13th, the bombardment was kept up, and in the light of the "rockets red glare, the bombs bursting in air" they could see the American flag still waving over the old fort. And when, in the first rays of dawn of September 14th, he still beheld the same glorious banner waving from its accustomed place, Francis Scott Key wrote the words of that wonderful song "The Star Spangled Banner."

The next day Key went ashore, and, after copying his poem, showed it to a friend and relative, Judge Nicholson, who saw its worth and at his suggestion it was printed. Soon after it was adapted to an English air known as "To Anacreon in Heaven," the composition of which is credited to John Stafford Smith, who is supposed to have written the music some time between 1770 and 1775. "The Star-Spangled Banner" was first sung in public by Ferdinand Durang, an actor, in a tavern near the Holiday Street Theatre in Baltimore, Md.

Francis Scott Key was the son of John Ross Key, an officer of the Revolutionary Army. He was born August 1, 1779, and died January 11, 1843, leaving "The Star-Spangled Banner" as a monument to his patriotic spirit, and an inspiration to his countrymen.

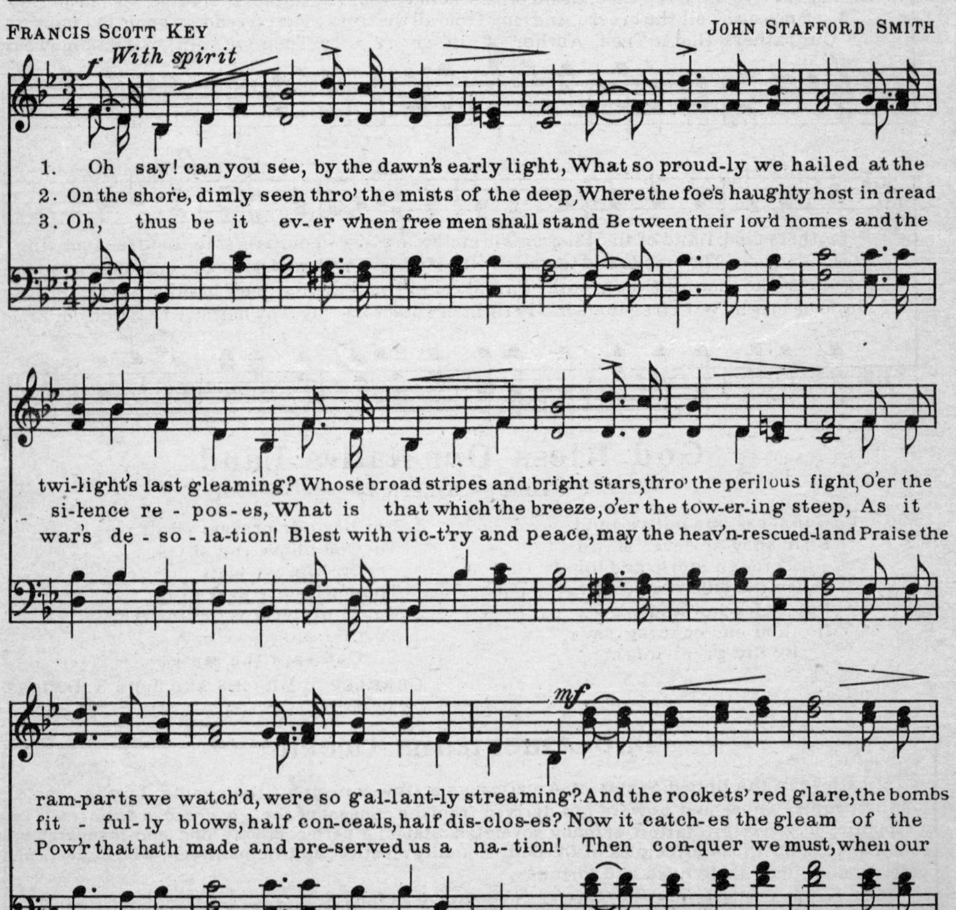
FRANCIS SCOTT KEY
JOHN STAFFORD SMITH
With spirit
1. Oh say! can you see, by the dawn's early light, What so proud-ly we hailed at the
2. On the shore, dimly seen thro' the mists of the deep, Where the foe's haughty host in dread
3. Oh, thus be it ev-er when free men shall stand Between their lov'd homes and the
twi-light's last gleaming? Whose broad stripes and bright stars, thro' the perilous fight, O'er the
si-lence re-pos-es, What is that which the breeze, o'er the tow-er-ing steep, As it
war's de-so-la-tion! Blest with vic-t'ry and peace, may the heav'n-rescued-land Praise the
ram-parts we watch'd, were so gal-lant-ly streaming? And the rockets' red glare, the bombs
fit-ful-ly blows, half con-ceals, half dis-clos-es? Now it catch-es the gleam of the
Pow'r that hath made and pre-served us a na-tion! Then con-quer we must, when our

M1977.C5
G65
1923
cop.2
Music
5
The Star-Spangled Banner—Continued
CHORUS
ff
bursting in air, Gave proof thro' the night that our flag was still there. Oh, say, does that
morning's first beam, In full glory re-flect-ed now shines on the stream; 'Tis the Star-spangled
cause it is just, And this be our mot-to: "In God is our trust!" And the Star-spangled
fff
Star-span-gled Ban-ner yet wave O'er the land of the free and the home of the brave?
Ban-ner, oh, long may it wave O'er the land of the free and the home of the brave!
Ban-ner in triumph shall wave O'er the land of the free and the home of the brave!
Flag Of The Free
UNKNOWN
ARR. FROM WAGNER
Brisk march time
1. Flag of the free, fair-est to see, Borne thro' the strife and the thunder of war;
2. Flag of the brave, long may it wave, Chos-en of God while His might we adore; In
Fine.
Ban-ner so bright with star-ry light, Float ev-er proud-ly from mountain to shore
Lib-er-ty's van, for manhood of man, Sym-bol of Right thro' the years passing o'er
D. S. While thro' the sky loud rings the cry, Un-ion and Lib-er-ty! one ev-er-more!
D. S.
Emblem of Freedom, hope to the slave, Spread thy fair folds but to shield and to save,
Pride of our country, honored a-far, Scat-ter each cloud that would darken a star,

Columbia, The Gem Of The Ocean

Columbia, the Gem of the Ocean is of uncertain origin. The melody has been claimed as of English composition, under the name of "Brittania, the Pride of the Ocean." The text was written at the request of David T. Shaw for a benefit, by Thomas a'Becket of the Chestnut Street Theatre, who rearranged and added the present beginning and ending to it. The date has been given by the latter as the fall of 1843.

THOMAS A'BECKET

Majestically
1. O Co-lum-bia, the gem of the o-cean, The home of the brave and the free,
2. When war wing'd its wide des-o-la-tion, And threaten'd the land to de-form,
3. The star-spangled banner bring hither, O'er Columbia's true sons let it wave;
The shrine of each patriot's de-vo-tion, A world offers homage to thee.
The ark then of freedom's foundation, Co - lumbia rode safe thro' the storm:
May the wreaths they have won never wither, Nor its stars cease to shine on the brave:
Thy mandates make heroes assemble, When Lib-er-ty's form stands in view;
With her garlands of vic-t'ry a-round her, When so proudly she bore her brave crew;
May thy serv-ice, u - nit-ed ne'er sev-er, But hold to their col-ors so true;
Thy ban-ners make tyr-an-ny tremble, When borne by the red, white, and blue!
With her flag proudly floating before her, The boast of the red, white, and blue!
The ar-my and na - vy for - ev - er, Three cheers for the red, white, and blue!
CHORUS
When borne by the red, white, and blue! When borne by the red, white, and blue!
The boast of the red, white, and blue! The boast of the red, white, and blue!
Three cheers for the red, white, and blue! Three cheers for the red, white, and blue!

Columbia The Gem Of The Ocean—Continued

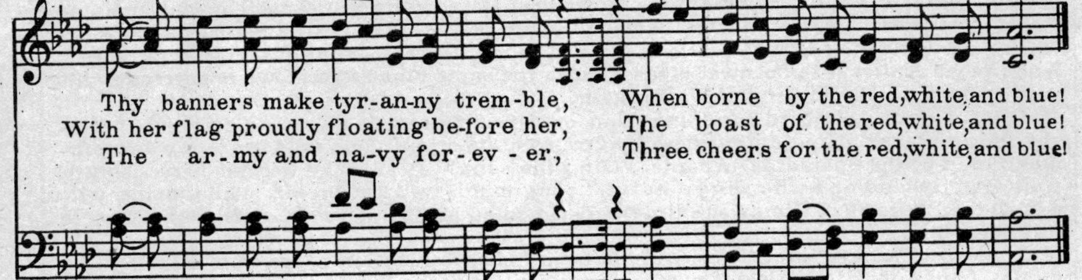
Thy banners make tyr-an-ny trem-ble, When borne by the red, white, and blue!
With her flag proudly floating be-fore her, The boast of the red, white, and blue!
The ar-my and na-vy for-ev-er, Three cheers for the red, white, and blue!

America, The Beautiful

(Tune—"Materna")

The words of this song were written in the summer of 1893 by Katherine Lee Bates upon her return from her first trip to the summit of Pike's Peak where the opening lines had been inspired by the beautiful view of "spacious skies" and "purple mountain majesties." They were first printed in a magazine on July 4th, 1895 and were soon after set to music. They have been sung to numerous tunes, but the one given below "Materna," by Samuel A. Ward, is the best known and the one to which "America the Beautiful" is at present most often sung.

KATHERINE LEE BATES　　　　SAMUEL A. WARD

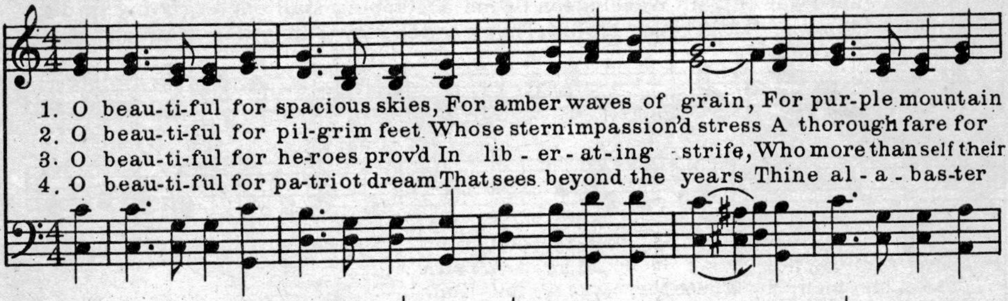

1. O beau-ti-ful for spacious skies, For amber waves of grain, For pur-ple mountain
2. O beau-ti-ful for pil-grim feet Whose sternimpassion'd stress A thorough fare for
3. O beau-ti-ful for he-roes prov'd In lib-er-at-ing strife, Who more than self their
4. O beau-ti-ful for pa-triot dream That sees beyond the years Thine al-a-bas-ter

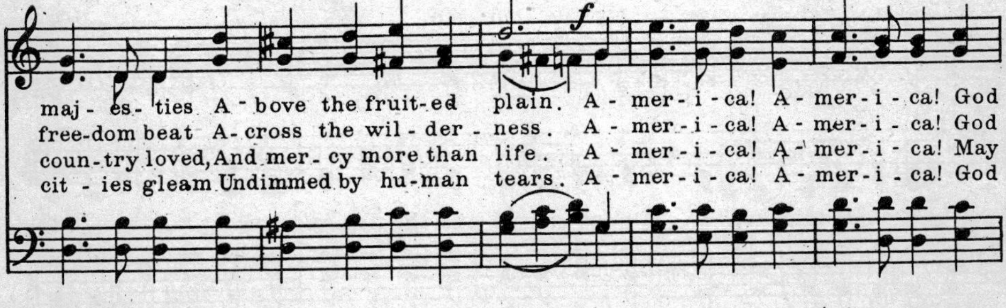

maj-es-ties A-bove the fruit-ed plain. A-mer-i-ca! A-mer-i-ca! God
free-dom beat A-cross the wil-der-ness. A-mer-i-ca! A-mer-i-ca! God
coun-try loved, And mer-cy more than life. A-mer-i-ca! A-mer-i-ca! May
cit-ies gleam Undimmed by hu-man tears. A-mer-i-ca! A-mer-i-ca! God

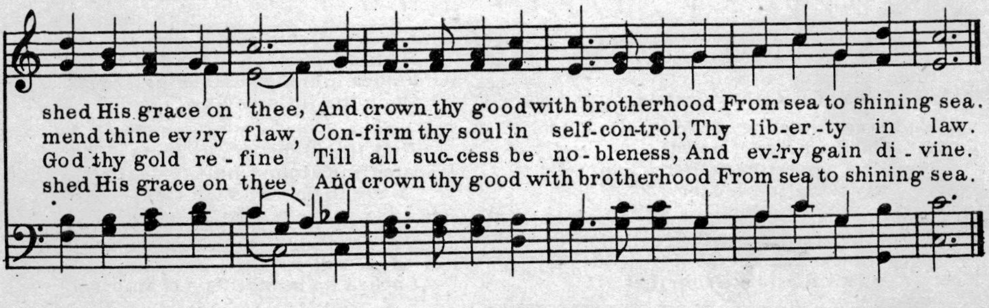

shed His grace on thee, And crown thy good with brotherhood From sea to shining sea.
mend thine ev'ry flaw, Con-firm thy soul in self-con-trol, Thy lib-er-ty in law.
God thy gold re-fine Till all suc-cess be no-bleness, And ev'ry gain di-vine.
shed His grace on thee, And crown thy good with brotherhood From sea to shining sea.

Yankee Doodle

When the Revolutionary War began, the colonists had no national hymn. We are told that during the French and Indian War a Dr. Richard Shackburg in a spirit of dirision gave to the poorly clad and awkward colonial soldiers the words and music of "Yankee Doodle," telling them it was a fine martial tune. When they played it the British were greatly amused. Twenty years after these same militiamen marched to victory at Lexington to this much derided tune, while their British teachers skulked behind fences or sought refuge in retreat. And five years after this Cornwallis marched to the same tune at Yorktown to surrender his sword and his army to General Washington.

Little is known of the history of the tune or of the origin of its name. No doubt it is several hundred years old, but authorities disagree as to its origin. One says the tune was commonly used by the Spaniards. Another claims the song was sung by German harvesters who worked in Holland and who sang a harvest song to this well known air, while another tells us that the Puritans of Cromwell's time were ridiculed as "Naukeys" in a stanza adapted to this same tune.

The word "Yankee" is sometimes given as an Indian corruption of the word English. Or, as has been said, it was a contemptuous term applied to the Puritans. Others claim it to be a cant word, expressing excellence, which originated in New England, but which finally came to be applied to the people of that region as a derisive epithet. "Doodle," according to the dictionaries, means a trifling or simple fellow.

The words which were applied to this tune by the colonists were little more than meaningless doggerel, and are little known now. It is not the lofty sentiment of the words, but the catchy, rollicking tune and the sacred associations, which give this song its place among our national songs.

Dr. SHACKBURG | UNKNOWN

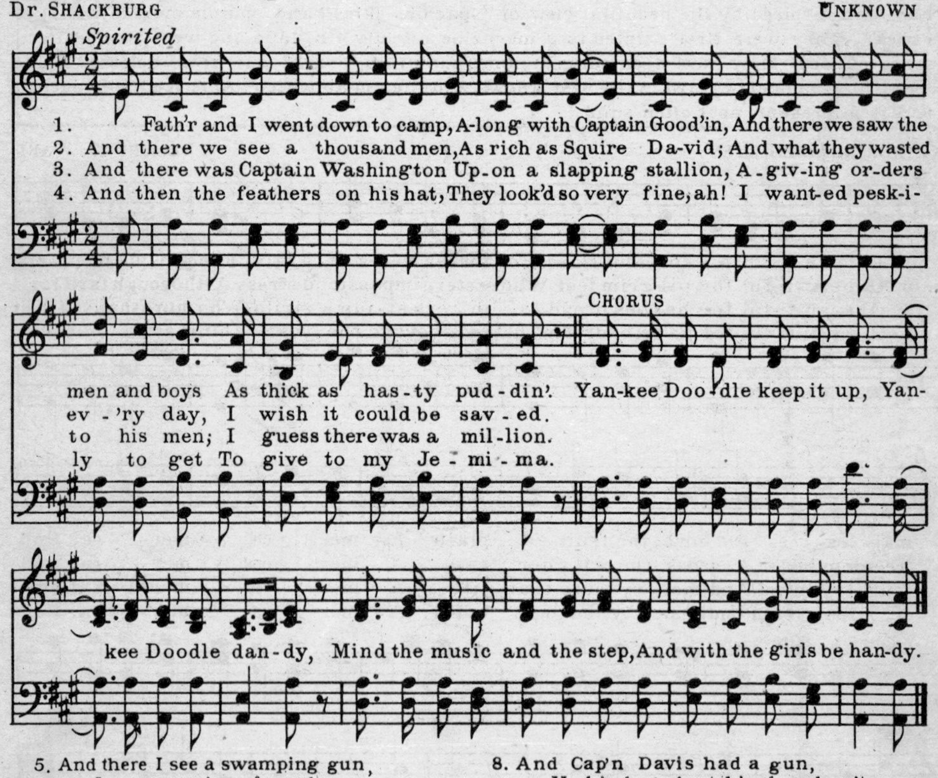
Spirited
1. Fath'r and I went down to camp, A-long with Captain Good'in, And there we saw the
2. And there we see a thousand men, As rich as Squire Da-vid; And what they wasted
3. And there was Captain Washington Up-on a slapping stallion, A-giv-ing or-ders
4. And then the feathers on his hat, They look'd so very fine, ah! I want-ed pesk-i-
men and boys As thick as has-ty pud-din'.
ev-'ry day, I wish it could be sav-ed.
to his men; I guess there was a mil-lion.
ly to get To give to my Je-mi-ma.
CHORUS
Yan-kee Doo-dle keep it up, Yan-kee Doodle dan-dy, Mind the music and the step, And with the girls be han-dy.

5. And there I see a swamping gun,
Large as a log of maple,
Upon a mighty little cart;
A load for father's cattle.

6. And every time they fired it off,
It took a horn of powder;
It made a noise like father's gun
Only a nation louder.

7. And there I see a little keg,
Its head all made of leather,
They knocked upon't with little sticks,
To call the folks together.

8. And Cap'n Davis had a gun,
He kind o' clapt his hand on't
And stuck a crooked stabbing-iron
Upon the little end on't.

9. The troopers, too, would gallop up
And fire right in our faces;
It scared me almost half to death
To see them run such races.

10. It scared me so I hooked it off,
Nor stopped, as I remember,
Nor turned about till I got home,
Locked up in mother's chamber.

Hail, Columbia!

The music of this song, originally known as "The Washington March," is generally attributed to Philip Phile. It was written in 1789 as an inaugural march for George Washington. The words were written nine years later by Joseph Hopkinson for a special occasion. At the time, England and France were at war and Americans were being divided by their sympathies for one or the other of these countries. No allusion is made in this song to either of the countries but its purpose was to keep Americans united. This sentiment has won for "Hail, Columbia!" a place among our national songs.

JOSEPH HOPKINSON | Attributed to PHILIP PHILE

Majestically
1. Hail, Co-lum-bia, hap-py land! Hail, ye heroes! heav'n-born band! Who fought and bled in
2. Im-mor-tal pa-triots! rise once more, Defend your rights, defend your shore; Let no rude foe with
3. Sound, sound the trump of fame! Let Wash-ington's great name Ring thro' the world with
4. Be-hold the Chief who now commands, Once more to serve his country stands, The rock on which the
Freedom's cause, Who fought and bled in Freedom's cause, And when the storm of war was gone, En-
im - pious hand, Let no rude foe with impious hand, In-vade the shrine where sacred lies, Of
loud applause, Ring thro' the world with loud applause; Let ev-'ry clime to free-dom dear
storm will beat, The rock on which the storm will beat; But armed in virtue, firm and true, His
joyed the peace your val-or won. Let in-de-pen-dence be our boast, Ev-er mind-ful
toil and blood the well earn'd prize. While off'ring peace, sincere and just, In heav'n we place a
Lis-ten with a joy-ful ear. With e-qual skill, with God-like pow'r, He governs in the
hopes are fixed on heav'n and you. When hope was sinking in dismay, When gloom obscur'd Co-
CHORUS
what it cost; Ev-er grate-ful for the prize, Let its al-tar reach the skies.
manly trust, That Truth and Justice will prevail, And ev'ry scheme of bondage fail.
fear-ful hour Of horrid war; or guides with ease The happier times of honest peace.
lumbia's day, His steady mind, from changes free, Resolv'd on death or liber-ty.
Firm, united,
let us be, Rallying round our liber-ty; As a band of brothers joined, Peace and safety
we shall find.

Dixie

"Dixie Land," or "Dixie," as it is generally called, the most popular of the songs of the South, was written by Daniel D. Emmett, of Ohio. In 1859, Mr. Emmett was a member of "Bryant's Minstrels," then playing in New York. One Saturday evening he was asked by Mr. Bryant to furnish a new song to be used in the performances the following week. On Monday morning Mr. Emmett took to the rehearsal the words and music of "Dixie", The song soon became the favorite all over the land. In 1860, an entertainment was given in New Orleans. The leader had some difficulty in selecting a march for his chorus. After trying several he decided upon. "Dixie." It was taken up by the people, sung upon the streets and soon carried to the battlefields, where it became the great inspirational song of the Southern Army.

Many different words were written to the tune. Those by Albert Pike, of Arkansas, were much used and are, perhaps, the most worthy of mention.

Like "Yankee Doodle," (with which it holds a close place), the original words of "Dixie" voice no great patriotic sentiment, and the music is not of a lofty character. Yet, like its companion, its notes stirred the hearts and crystallized souls who fought for the "Flag of Dixie."

Today, to the music of these two strange songs, there echoes the tread of a united people whose hearts are moved alike by the stirring strains, and who as they listen are ready to say with uplifted hands, bared brows, and reverent lips, "We give our heads and our hearts to God, and our Country."

D.D.E.
DAN D. EMMETT
Lively
1. I wish I was in de land ob cot-ton,
2. Dar's buck-wheat cakes an' In-gen bat-ter,
Old times dar am not forgotten, Look a-way! Look a-way! Look a-way! Dixie
Makes you fat, or a lit-tle fatter, Look a-way! Look a-way! Look a-way! Dixie
Land. In Dix-ie Land whar I was born in, Ear-ly on one
Land. Den hoe it down an' scratch your grabble, To Dix-ie Land I'm

Dixie—Continued

frost-y mornin', Look a-way! Look a - way! Look a-way! Dix-ie Land!
bound to trabble, Look a-way! Look a - way! Look a - way! Dix-ie Land!
CHORUS
Den I wish I was in Dix-ie, Hoo-ray! (hooray) Hoo-ray! (hooray) In Dixie Land, I'll
take my stand to lib and die in Dix-ie; A - way, A - way, A -
A - way, a - way,
way down south in Dixie, A-way, A-way, A-way down south in Dixie.
A - way, a-way,

In the chorus of Dixie, where the melody is given to the bass voices, the sopranos may take those notes two octaves higher than written, if it seems best to have the sopranos on the melody throughout the song.

Battle Hymn of the Republic

Julia Ward Howe, the author of this stirring war song, was born in New York, May 27, 1819, and was married to Dr. S.G. Howe in 1843.

In December, 1861, Dr. and Mrs. Howe, with a party of friends, paid a visit to Washington. Everything about the city had a martial aspect. The railroads were guarded by pickets, the streets were full of soldiers and all about could be seen the "watchfires of a hundred circling camps."

One day the party drove several miles from the city to see a review of the Federal soldiers. An attack by the Confederates caused much excitement and delayed their return. Finally they started back to Washington under an escort of soldiers, and to while away the time they sang war songs, among others, "John Brown."

Waking in the gray dawn of the following morning Mrs. Howe found herself weaving together words to the music she had sung the day before. Fearing she might forget the lines if she slept again, she arose and wrote down the verses of the "Battle Hymn of the Republic." The poem was first published in the Atlantic Monthly for February, 1862. The verses were published without the author's name, and she received but five dollars for them.

Of this great hymn a recent writer says, "Unlike many of the songs of the Civil War, it contains nothing sectional, nothing personal, nothing of a temporary character. While we feel the beauty of the lines and their aspiration after freedom, even in the piping times of peace, it is only in the time of storm and stress that their full meaning shines out. Written with intense feeling, they seem to burn and glow when our own emotions are aroused."

JULIA WARD HOWE
WILLIAM STEFFE
Moderate march time
1. Mine eyes have seen the glo-ry of the com-ing of the Lord; He is tramp-ling out the vint-age where the grapes of wrath are stor'd; He hath loos'd the fateful light-ning of His ter-ri-ble swift sword: His truth is march-ing on.
2. I have seen Him in the watch-fires of a hun-dred cir-cling camps, They have build-ed Him an al-tar in the evening dews and damps; I can read His righteous sen-tence by the dim and flar-ing lamps: His day is march-ing on.
3. I have read a fi-ery gos-pel writ in bur-nished rows of steel: "As ye deal with My con-tem-ners, so with you My grace shall deal:" Let the He-ro born of wom-an crush the ser-pent with His heel, Since God is march-ing on.
4. He has sound-ed forth the trumpet that shall nev-er call re-treat; He is sift-ing out the hearts of men be-fore His judgment seat. Oh, be swift, my soul, to an-swer Him! be ju-bi-lant, my feet! Our God is march-ing on.
5. In the beau-ty of the lil-ies Christ was born a-cross the sea, With a glo-ry in His bos-om that trans-figures you and me; As He died to make men ho-ly let us die to make men free, While God is march-ing on.
CHORUS
Glo-ry, glo-ry, hal-le-lu-jah! Glo-ry, glo-ry, hal-le-lu-jah!

Battle Hymn of the Republic — Continued

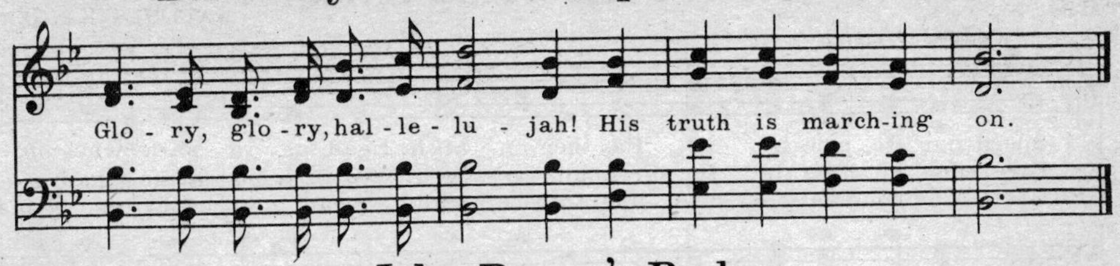
Glo - ry, glo - ry, hal - le - lu - jah! His truth is march-ing on.

John Brown's Body

(Tune–Battle Hymn of the Republic)

1.
John Brown's body lies amould'ring in the grave,
John Brown's body lies amould'ring in the grave,
John Brown's body lies amould'ring in the grave,
His soul goes marching on!
Chorus:

2.
The stars of heaven are looking kindly down,
The stars of heaven are looking kindly down,
The stars of heaven are looking kindly down,
On the grave of old John Brown!
Chorus:

3.
He's gone to be a soldier in the army of the Lord,
He's gone to be a soldier in the army of the Lord,
He's gone to be a soldier in the army of the Lord,
His soul is marching on!
Chorus:

4.
John Brown's knapsack is strapped upon his back,
John Brown's knapsack is strapped upon his back,
John Brown's knapsack is strapped upon his back,
His soul is marching on!
Chorus:

Chorus: Glory, glory, hallelujah! Glory, glory, hallelujah!
Glory, glory, hallelujah! His soul is marching on.

The Vacant Chair

H. S. WASHBURN — GEORGE F. ROOT

With feeling

1. We shall meet, but we shall miss him, There will be one vacant chair; We shall lin-ger to ca-
2. At our fire-side, sad and lone-ly, Of-ten will the bosom swell At remembrance of the
3. True, they tell us wreaths of glory Evermore will deck his brow, But this sooth's the anguish

D. C. We shall meet, but we shall miss him, There will be one vacant chair; We shall lin-ger to ca-

Fine.

ress him, When we breathe our ev'ning pray'r. When a year a - go we gather'd, Joy was
sto - ry How our no - ble Wil-lie fell; How he strove to bear our banner Thro' the
on - ly Sweeping o'er our heartstrings now. Sleep to-day, O ear-ly fall-en, In thy

ress him, When we breathe our evening pray'r.

D. C.

in his mild blue eye, But a gold-en cord is severed, And our hopes in ru-in lie.
thick-est of the fight, And up-hold our country's honor, In the strength of manhood's might.
green and narrow bed, Dirges from the pine and cypress Mingle with the tears we shed.

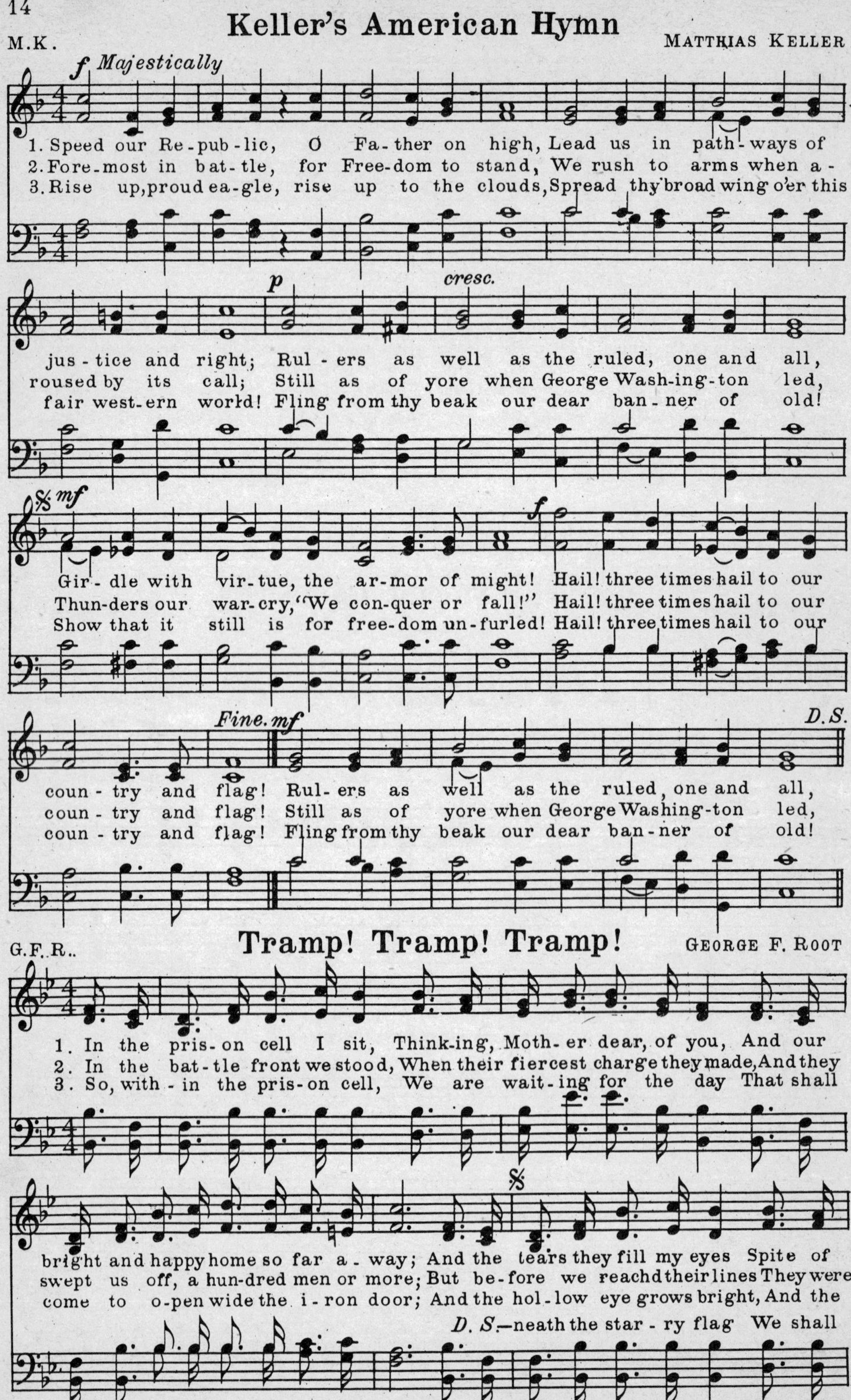
Keller's American Hymn
M.K.
MATTHIAS KELLER
f Majestically
1. Speed our Re-pub-lic, O Fa-ther on high, Lead us in path-ways of
2. Fore-most in bat-tle, for Free-dom to stand, We rush to arms when a-
3. Rise up, proud ea-gle, rise up to the clouds, Spread thy broad wing o'er this
p
cresc.
jus-tice and right; Rul-ers as well as the ruled, one and all,
roused by its call; Still as of yore when George Wash-ing-ton led,
fair west-ern world! Fling from thy beak our dear ban-ner of old!
mf
Gir-dle with vir-tue, the ar-mor of might! Hail! three times hail to our
Thun-ders our war-cry, "We con-quer or fall!" Hail! three times hail to our
Show that it still is for free-dom un-furled! Hail! three times hail to our
f
Fine. mf
D.S.
coun-try and flag! Rul-ers as well as the ruled, one and all,
coun-try and flag! Still as of yore when George Washing-ton led,
coun-try and flag! Fling from thy beak our dear ban-ner of old!
Tramp! Tramp! Tramp!
G.F.R..
GEORGE F. ROOT
1. In the pris-on cell I sit, Think-ing, Moth-er dear, of you, And our
2. In the bat-tle front we stood, When their fiercest charge they made, And they
3. So, with-in the pris-on cell, We are wait-ing for the day That shall
bright and happy home so far a-way; And the tears they fill my eyes Spite of
swept us off, a hun-dred men or more; But be-fore we reachd their lines They were
come to o-pen wide the i-ron door; And the hol-low eye grows bright, And the
D. S.—neath the star-ry flag We shall

Tramp! Tramp! Tramp!—Continued

Fine.
all that I can do, Though I try to cheer my com-rades and be gay.
beat-en back dis-mayed, And we heard the cry of vic-t'ry o'er and o'er.
poor heart al-most gay, As we think of see-ing home and friends once more.
breathe the air a-gain Of the free-land in our own be-lov-ed home.
CHORUS
D.S.
Tramp, tramp, tramp, the boys are marching, Cheer up, comrades, they will come, And be-
marching on, O cheer up, com-rades, they will come,
Tenting On The Old Camp Ground
W.K.
Moderately.
WALTER KITTREDGE
1. We're tent-ing to night on the old Camp ground, Give us a song to cheer
2. We've been tent-ing to night on the old Camp ground, Thinking of days gone by,
3. We are tired of war on the old Camp ground, Man-y are dead and gone,
4. We've been fight-ing to-day on the old Camp ground, Man-y are ly-ing near;
Our wear-y hearts, a song of home And friends we love so dear.
Of the loved ones at home that gave us the hand, And the tear that said, "Good-bye."
Of the brave and true who've left their homes, Oth-ers been wounded long.
Some are dead, and some are dy-ing Man-y are in tears.
CHORUS
Man-y are the hearts that are weary to-night, Wishing for the war to cease; Man-y are the hearts that are
looking for the right, To see the dawn of peace. Tenting to-night, Tenting to-night, Tenting on the old camp-ground.

The Battle Cry Of Freedom

G. F. R. GEORGE F. ROOT

1. Yes, we'll ral-ly round the flag boys, we'll rally once again, Shouting the battle cry of
2. We are springing to the call of our brothers gone before, Shouting the battle cry of
3. We will wel-come to our numbers the loyal, true and brave, Shouting the battle cry of
4. So we're springing to the call from the East and from the West, Shouting the battle cry of

Freedom; We will rally from the hillside, we'll gather from the plain, Shouting the battle cry of Freedom.
Freedom; And we'll fill the vacant ranks with a million free men more, Shouting the battle cry of Freedom.
Freedom; And al-tho' they may be poor, not a man shall be a slave, Shouting the battle cry of Freedom.
Freedom; And we'll prove a loy - al crew for the land we love the best, Shouting the battle cry of Freedom.

CHORUS

The Union for-ev-er, hurrah, boys, Hurrah! Down with the traitor, Up with the star; While we

ral-ly round the flag, boys, rally once a-gain, Shouting the bat-tle cry of Free- dom.

Just Before The Battle, Mother

G. F. R. GEORGE. F. ROOT

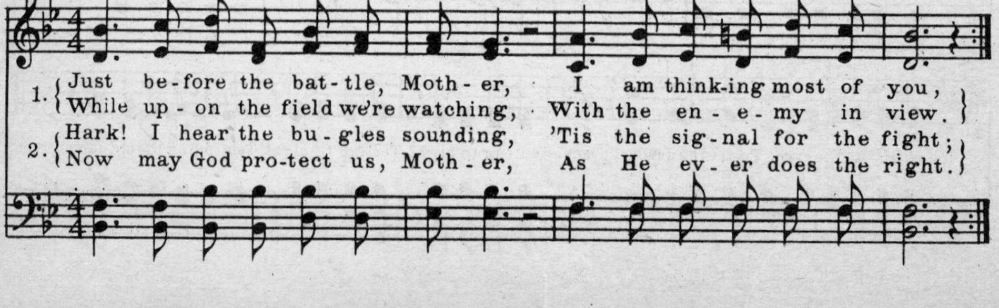

1. Just be-fore the bat-tle, Moth-er, I am think-ing most of you,
While up - on the field we're watching, With the en - e - my in view.
2. Hark! I hear the bu-gles sounding, 'Tis the sig-nal for the fight;
Now may God pro-tect us, Moth - er, As He ev - er does the right.

Just Before The Battle, Mother—Continued

Com-rades brave are round me ly-ing, Fill'd with thot's of home and God; For
Hear the "Bat-tle Cry of Free dom," How it swells up-on the air; Oh,
well they know that on the mor-row Some will sleep be-neath the sod.
yes, we'll ral-ly round the standard, Or we'll per-ish no-bly there.
CHORUS
Fare-well, Moth-er, you may never Press me to your heart a-gain; But
(you may never, Mother,)
rit.
oh, you'll not for-get me, Mother, If I'm number'd with the slain.
(you will not forget me)

Civil War Songs

The nine foregoing songs, and "When Johnny Comes Marching Home," which follows, are among those which came into existence during the Civil War. Because each embodies some typical sentiment of the time, it holds a place among our popular national songs

The stories of "Dixie," "Battle Hymn of the Republic," and "John Brown's Body" have been previously given.

"Keller's American Hymn" attracted little notice during the Civil War but in 1872, at a Peace Festival, it was featured and became well known. It stands as a guiding principle of what we would like our country to be.

"Tenting on the Old Camp Ground" was written, composed and first sung by Walter Kittredge as his patriotic contribution after he had failed to pass the physical examination for entrance into the Union Army.

"When Johnny Comes Marching Home" is a stirring number popular ever since the Civil War when it was composed. The name of the author and composer, "Louis Lambert," was a nom de plume used by Patrick S. Gilmore, famous as a band leader and promoter of festivals and jubilees.

George F. Root contributed "Tramp! Tramp! Tramp!" "The Battle Cry of Freedom," "Just Before the Battle Mother," and with Henry F. Washburn, he wrote "The Vacant Chair."

All of these songs were written under the influence of emotions excited by the Civil War. Today, after our more recent war experience, they take on a newer and deeper meaning.

When Johnny Comes Marching Home

L.L.
SOLO
With spirit
CHORUS
SOLO
LOUIS LAMBERT
1. When Johnny comes marching home again, Hurrah, hur-rah! We'll give him a heart-y
2. The old church bell will peal with joy, Hurrah, hur-rah! To wel-come home our
3. Get rea - dy for the Ju-bi-lee, Hurrah, hur-rah! We'll give the he-ro
ff
p
CHORUS
SOLO
wel-come then, Hur-rah; hur-rah! The men will cheer, the boys will shout, The
dar-ling boy, Hur-rah, hur-rah! The vil-lage lads and las-sies say, With
three times three; Hur-rah, hur-rah! The lau-rel wreath is rea-dy now To
ff
p
CHORUS Repeat at lib.
la-dies, they will all turn out, And we'll all feel gay, When Johnny comes marching home.
roses they will strew the way, And we'll all feel gay, When Johnny comes marching home.
place up-on his loy-al brow; And we'll all feel gay, When Johnny comes marching home.

A National Prayer

O God of purity and peace, God of light and freedom, God of comfort and joy, we thank thee for our country, this great land of hope, whose wide doors thou hast opened to so many millions that struggle with hardship and with hunger in the crowded Old World.

We give thanks to the power that has made and preserved us a nation, that has carried our ship of state through storm and darkness and has given us a place of honor and power that we might bear aloft the standard of impartial liberty and impartial law.

May our altars and our schools ever stand as pillars of welfare; may the broad land be filled with homes of intelligent and contented industry, that through the long generations our land may be a happy land and our country a power of good will among the nations. *Amen.*

CHARLES GORDON AMES

Keep The Home Fires Burning

LENA GUILBERT FORD — IVOR NOVELLO

March time

1. They were summon'd from the hill-side, They were call'd in from the glen, And the Coun-try found them ready at the stir-ring call for men (the stir-ring call for men) Let no tears add to their hard-ships, As the sol-diers pass a-long, And al-though your heart is break-ing, Make it sing this cheer-y song.

2. O-ver seas they came a-plead-ing, "Help a na-tion in dis-tress!" And we gave our glo-rious lad-dies; Honor bade us do no less, (and bade us do no less) For no gal-lant son of free-dom To a ty-rant's yoke should bend; And a no-ble heart must an-swer To the sa-cred call of "Friend."

CHORUS

Keep the Home-fires burn-ing While your hearts are yearn-ing, Tho' your lads are far a-way They dream of home.

There's a sil-ver lin-ing Thro' the dark clouds shin-ing, Turn the dark cloud in-side out, Till the boys come home.

Anvil Chorus

(From the opera, Il Trovatore)

CAMMANARO

GIUSEPPI VERDI

Quickly

p

1

2 FULL CHORUS IN UNISON

God of the na-tions, in glo-ry en-thron-ed, Upon our lov'd country Thy blessings

pp

pour; Guide us and guard us from strife in the future, Let Peace dwell among us for ever-

pp

Anvil Chorus – Continued

CHORUS IN UNISON
ANVILS
Proud - ly our
bann - er now gleams with gold - en lus - tre! Bright - er each
star shines in the glo - rious clus - ter! Lib - er -
ty for - ev - er - more! And Peace and Un - ion, And Peace and
Un - ion, throughout our hap - py land. land.
f
ff
D.C.
1
2

Years Of Peace

SICILIAN MARINERS' AIR
1. Years are com - ing, speed them on - ward!
2. Earth has heard too long of bat - tle,
3. Years are com - ing when for - ev - er,
When the sword shall gath - er rust, And the hel - met,
Heard the trum - pet's voice too long; But an - oth - er
War's dread ban - ner shall be furled, And the an - gel,
lance and fal - chion, Sleep at last in __ si - lent dust!
age ad - van - ces, Seers fore - told in __ an - cient song.
Peace, be wel - comed, Reg - ent of the __ hap - py world.
O God, Beneath Thy Guiding Hand
LEONARD BACON
JOHN HATTON
1. O God, be-neath Thy guid-ing hand, Our ex-iled fa-thers cross'd the sea;
2. Thou heard'st, well pleas'd, the song, the pray'r: Thy blessing came; and still its pow'r
3. Laws, freedom, truth, and faith in God Came with those exiles o'er the waves;
4. And here Thy name, O God of love, Their children's children shall a-dore,
And when they trod the win-t'ry strand, With pray'r and psalm they worship'd Thee.
Shall on-ward, thro' all a - ges bear The mem'ry of that ho-ly hour.
And where their pil-grim feet have trod, The God they trusted guards their graves.
Till these e - ter - nal hills re - move, And spring a-dorns the earth no more.

Praise for Peace

ANGUS S. HIBBARD — FRIEDRICH F. FLEMMING

1. Fa - ther in Heav - en, in Thy love a - bound - ing, Hear these Thy chil - dren thro' the world re - sound - ing, Loud in Thy prais - es thanks for peace a - bid - ing, Ev - er a - bid - ing.
2. Filled be our hearts with peace be - yond com - par - ing, Peace in Thy world, joy to all heart's des - pair - ing, Firm is our trust in Thee for peace en - dur - ing, Ev - er en - dur - ing.
3. God of our Fa - thers strength - en ev - 'ry na - tion, In Thy great peace where on - ly is sal - va - tion, So may the world its fu - ture spread be - fore Thee, Thus to a - dore Thee.

Integer Vitae

The Latin words, which are two stanzas from Horace's XXII Ode, may be sung to the music of "Praise for Peace." A rather free translation of the Latin is also given.

Using the Latin words, the song is a very effective number for male voices.

Integer vitae scelerisque purus
Non eget Mauris jaculis, neque arcu,
Neque venenatis gravida sagittis,
Fusce, pharetra;

Sive per Syrtes iter aestuasas,
Sive facturus per inhospitalem
Caucasum, vel quae loca fabulosus
Lambit Hydaspes.

He who is noble, kind in thought and action,
Faithful to duty, pure, and single hearted,
Needs not a weapon, needs not man to guard him,
Virtue defends him.

What though he wander o'er the burning desert?
What though he journey o'er unfriendly mountain?
Sleeping or waking, though by death surrounded,
Virtue defends him.

Home, Sweet Home

While the United States has no great war song which ranks with those of other nations, it has one song of peace that reaches not only the hearts of its own people, but touches a responsive chord in the hearts of the whole world. The song is "Home, Sweet Home."

Its author, John Howard Payne, was born in New York City, June 9, 1792, and died at Tunis, April 10, 1852. Payne's mother died when he was thirteen, and after that the author of the world's home song never knew what it meant to have a home of his own.

At the age of thirteen Payne became a clerk in a mercantile house. At seventeen he went on the stage and achieved great success in the large eastern cities. He was twenty-one when he appeared in Drury Lane Theatre, London. He lived abroad for twenty years, and, altho he seemed to have been diligent and fairly successful, he was poor and often wretched.

He wrote several successful dramas, among them, "Clari, the Maid of Milan." At the suggestion of the manager of Covent Garden Theatre, the play was changed into an opera and the words of "Home, Sweet Home," were introduced into it. The song was a great success and enriched all who handled it except its author. He did not even receive the twenty-five pounds which was his share of the proceeds from the sale of the manuscript.

In 1832 Payne returned to America. Later he was appointed consul to Tunis and died there in 1852.

In 1883, through the generosity of W. W. Corcoran, the remains of John Howard Payne were brought to his native land and buried at Oak Hill Cemetary, Washington, D.C.

JOHN HOWARD PAYNE
HENRY R. BISHOP
1. 'Mid pleasures and pal - a - ces though we may roam, Be it ev - er so humble, there's no place like home; A charm from the skies seems to hal-low us there, Which, seek thro' the world, is ne'er met with else-where.
2. I gaze on the moon as I tread the drear wild, And feel that my mother now thinks of her child, As she looks on that moon from our own cottage door, Thro' the wood-bine whose fragrance shall cheer me no more.
3. An ex - ile from home splendor daz - zles in vain; Oh, give me my lowly thatched cottage a - gain; The birds singing gai - ly, that came at my call, Give me them, and that peace of mind dear-er than all.
Home, home, sweet, sweet home,
D.S. There's no place like home, Oh, there's no place like home.
The Bell Doth Toll
(Round)
Slowly
1
The bell doth toll, Its ech - oes roll, I know the sound full well;
2
I love its ring - ing, For it calls to sing - ing, With its bim, bim, bim, bom, bell,
3
Bim, bom, bim, bom, bell.

Old Black Joe

S. C. F.
STEPHEN C. FOSTER
1. Gone are the days when my heart was young and gay; Gone are my
2. Why do I weep when my heart should feel no pain? Why do I
3. Where are the hearts once so hap - py and so free? The chil - dren so
friends from the cot - ton fields a - way; Gone from the earth to a
sigh that my friends come not a - gain? Griev - ing for forms now de -
dear that I held up - on my knee? Gone to the shore where my
bet-ter land I know, I hear their gen-tle voic - es calling, "Old Black Joe!"
part-ed long a - go, I hear their gen-tle voic - es calling, "Old Black Joe!"
soul has long'd to go, I hear their gen-tle voic - es calling, "Old Black Joe!"
Fine.
mf
CHORUS
pp
D.S. al Fine.
I'm com ing, I'm com-ing, For my head is bend-ing low;

Stephen C. Foster

Stephen Collins Foster, a truly American writer of what may be called the folk-songs of America, was born July 4th, 1826 at Lawrenceburg, Pennsylvania, now a part of Pittsburgh, and died in New York in 1864. From an early age he was interested in music. He often attendend negro camp meetings and there studied the music of the colored people. His first success in composition was "Oh! Susannah". Soon after, he produced "My Old Kentucky Home" and "Massa's In The Cold, Cold Ground" which at once became popular.

"The Old Folks At Home" (Way down upon the Swanee River) is his masterpiece. A more tender song of home and its memories has never been written. Another of his songs which achieved great popularity is "Old Black Joe".

Chief among Foster's characteristics was his tenderness. This quality is reflected in all of his songs.

My Old Kentucky Home

S.C.F.
STEPHEN C. FOSTER
Rather slowly
1. The sun shines bright in the old Ken-tuck-y home, 'Tis sum-mer,
young folks roll on the lit-tle cab-in floor, All mer-ry,
2. They hunt no more for the pos-sum and the coon, On the mead-ow,
day goes by like a shadow o'er the heart, With sor-row
3. The head must bow and the back will have to bend, Wher - ev - er
few more days for to tote the wea-ry load, No mat-ter,
the dark-ies are gay; The corn-top's ripe and the mead-ow's in the bloom, While the
all hap-py and bright; By'n by hard times comes a knock-ing at the door, Then my
the hill and the shore; They sing no more by the glim-mer of the moon, On the
where all was de-light; The time has come when the darkies have to part, Then my
the dark-y may go; A few more days, and the trou-ble all will end, In the
'twill nev-er be light; A few more days till we tot-ter on the road, Then my
1. birds make mu-sic all the day; The
2. bench by the old cab-in door; The
3. field where the su-gar-canes grow; A
old Kentuck-y home, good night!
old Kentuck-y home, good night!
old Kentuck-y home, good night!
CHORUS
Weep no more, my la-dy, O weep no more to day! We will
rit.
sing one song for the old Ken-tucky home, For the old Kentucky home, far a-way.

Old Folks At Home

S. C. F.
STEPHEN C. FOSTER
1. { 'Way down up-on de Swa-nee Riv-er, Far, far a-way,
All up and down de whole cre-a-tion, Sad-ly I roam,
2. { All roun' de lit-tle farm I wan-dered, When I was young;
When I was play-ing with my broth-er, Hap-py was I;
3. { One lit-tle hut a-mong de bush-es, One that I love,
When will I see de bees a-hum-ming All roun' de comb?
Fine.
Dere's wha my heart is turn-ing ev-er, Dere's wha de old folks stay.
Still long-ing for de old plan-ta-tion, And for de old folks at home.
Den man-y hap-py days I squander'd, Man-y de songs I sung.
Oh! take me to my kind old moth-er, There let me live and die.
Still sad-ly to my mem-'ry rush-es, No mat-ter where I rove.
When will I hear de ban-jo tum-ming, Down in my good old home?
D.S.—Oh! darkies, how my heart grows weary, Far from de old folks at home.
REFRAIN
D.S.
All de world am sad and drear-y, Ev-'ry-where I roam;
Stars Of The Summer Night
HENRY W. LONGFELLOW
ISAAC B. WOODBURY
1. Stars of the sum-mer night, Far in yon az-ure deeps, Hide, hide your
2. Moon of the sum-mer night, Far down yon west-ern steeps, Sink, sink in
3. Dreams of the sum-mer night, Tell her, her lov-er keeps Watch while, in
gold-en light, She sleeps, my la-dy sleeps; She sleeps, She sleeps, my lady sleeps.
sil-ver light, She sleeps, my la-dy sleeps; She sleeps, She sleeps, my lady sleeps.
slumber light, She sleeps, my la-dy sleeps; She sleeps, She sleeps, my lady sleeps.

Hard Times Come Again No More
S.C.F.
STEPHEN C. FOSTER
mf Moderately
1. Let us pause in life's pleasures and count its many tears While we all sup sorrow with the
2. While we seek mirth and beauty and music light and gay There are frail forms fainting at the
poor: There's a song that will linger for-ev-er in our ears, "Oh! Hard Times, come again no more.
door: Tho' their voices are silent, their pleading looks will say: "Oh! Hard Times, come again no more."
CHORUS
'Tis the song, the sigh of the wea - ry; Hard Times, Hard Times, come again no more;
Many days you have linger'd a-round my cab-in door, Oh! Hard Times, come again no more.
slower
Old Dog Tray
S.C.F.
STEPHEN C. FOSTER
Moderately
1. The morn of life is past, And ev'ning comes at last, It brings me a dream of a
2. The forms I call'd my own, Have vanish'd one by one, The loved ones, the dear ones have
once hap - py day, Of mer-ry forms I've seen Up - on the vil-lage green,
all passed a way, Their happy smiles have flown, Their gentle voices gone; I've

Old Dog Tray—Continued
CHORUS
Sport-ing with my old dog Tray.
noth- ing left but old dog Tray.
Old dog Tray's ever faithful, Grief can-not drive him a-
way, He's gen-tle, he is kind; I'll nev er, nev er find A bet-ter friend than old dog Tray
Uncle Ned
S.C.F.
STEPHEN C. FOSTER
1. There was an old darkey and his name was Uncle Ned, And he died long ago, long a-go;
2. His fingers were long as the cane in the brake, And he had no eyes for to see;
3. One cold, frost-y morning, old Ned died, Massa's tears they fell like the rain;
He had no wool on the top of his head, In the place where the wool ought to grow.
And he had no teeth for to eat a hoe-cake, So he had to let the hoe-cake be.
For he knew when Ned was laid in the ground, He'd never see his like a - gain.
REFRAIN Bass Solo
Harmony
Then lay down the shov-el and the hoe, Hang up the fid-dle and the bow;
For there's no more work for poor old Ned, He's gone where the good darkies go.

Massa's In The Cold Ground
S.C.F.
STEPHEN C. FOSTER
1. Round de meadows am a-ringing De darkeys' mournful song, While de mocking birds am singing,
2. When de autumn leaves were falling, When de days were cold, 'Twas hard to hear old Massa calling,
3. Massa make de darkeys love him, Cayse he was so kind, Now dey sad-ly weep a-bove him,
Hap - py as de day am long. Where de i - vy am a-creep-ing, O'er de gras-sy mound,
Cayse he was so weak and old. Now de o-range trees am blooming, On de san-dy shore,
Mourning cayse he leave dem behind. I can-not work be-fore to-morrow, Cayse de tear drop now;
CHORUS
Dare old Mas-sa am a-sleep-ing, Sleep-ing in de cold, cold ground.
Now de summer days am coming, Mas-sa neb-ber calls no more.
I try to drive a-way my sor-row, Pick - ing on de old ban - jo.
Down in de cornfield
Hear dat mournful sound; All de darkeys am a-weep-ing, Mas-sa's in de cold, cold ground.
How Can I Leave Thee
FRIEDRICH KÜCKEN
1. How can I leave thee! How can I from thee part! Thou on-ly hast my heart, Dear one, be-lieve.
2. Blue is a flow'r-et Called the For-get-me-not, Wear it up-on thy heart, And think of me!
3. Would I a bird were! Soon at thy side to be, Fal-con nor hawk would fear, Speeding to thee.
Thou hast this soul of mine So closely bound to thine, No oth-er can I love Save thee a-lone!
Flow'ret and hope may die, Yet love with us shall stay, That can-not pass away, Dear one, be-lieve.
When, by the fow-ler slain, I at thy feet should lie, Thou sadly shouldst complain, Joyful I'd die.

Darling Nelly Gray
B.R.H.
B. R. Hanby
1. There's a low green val-ley on the old Ken-tuck-y shore, Where I've whiled many
2. When the moon had clim'd the mountain, and the stars were shining too, Then I'd take my
3. My eyes are get-ting blinded, And I can-not see my way; Hark! There's some bod-y
hap - py hours a-way, A sit-ting and a-sing-ing by the lit-tle cot-tage door
darl - ing Nel-ly Gray, And we'd float down the riv-'er in my lit-tle red ca - noe,
knock-ing at the door, O I hear the an-gels calling, and I see my Nel-ly Gray,
Where lived my darl-ing Nel-ly Gray.
While my ban - jo sweet-ly I would play.
Fare - well to the old Ken-tuck-y shore.
Chorus
O my poor Nel - ly Gray, they have
O my poor Nel - ly Gray, they have
O my darling Nel - ly Gray, up in
1-2. tak-en you a-way, And I'll nev-er see my darl-ing an-y more; I'm sit-ting by the
3. heaven there, they say, That they'll never take you from me any more; I'm a coming—coming—
riv-er and I'm weeping all the day, For you've gone from the old Kentucky shore.
coming, as the an-gels clear the way, Fare - well to the old Kentucky shore.
Good Night
(Round)
1
2
3
Good night to you all, and sweet be thy sleep; May an-gels a -
round you their si - lent watch keep, Good night, good night, good night, good night.

Carry Me Back To Old Virginny
J. B.
JAMES BLAND
1. Car-ry me back to old Vir-ginny, There's where the cotton and the corn and taters grow,
2. Car-ry me back to old Vir-ginny, There let me live till I with-er and de-cay,
p
There's where the birds warble sweet in the spring-time, There's where the old darkey's
Long by the old Dis-mal Swamp have I wan dered, There's where this old darkey's
heart am long'd to go. There's where I la-bored so hard for old Mas-sa,
life will pass a-way. Mas - sa and Mis-sis have long gone be-fore me,
Day af-ter day in the field of yel-low corn, No place on earth do I
Soon we will meet on that bright and golden shore, There we'll be hap - py and
love more sin-cere-ly Than old Vir-gin-ny, the state where I was born.
free from all sor-row, There's where we'll meet and we'll nev- er part no more.
rit.

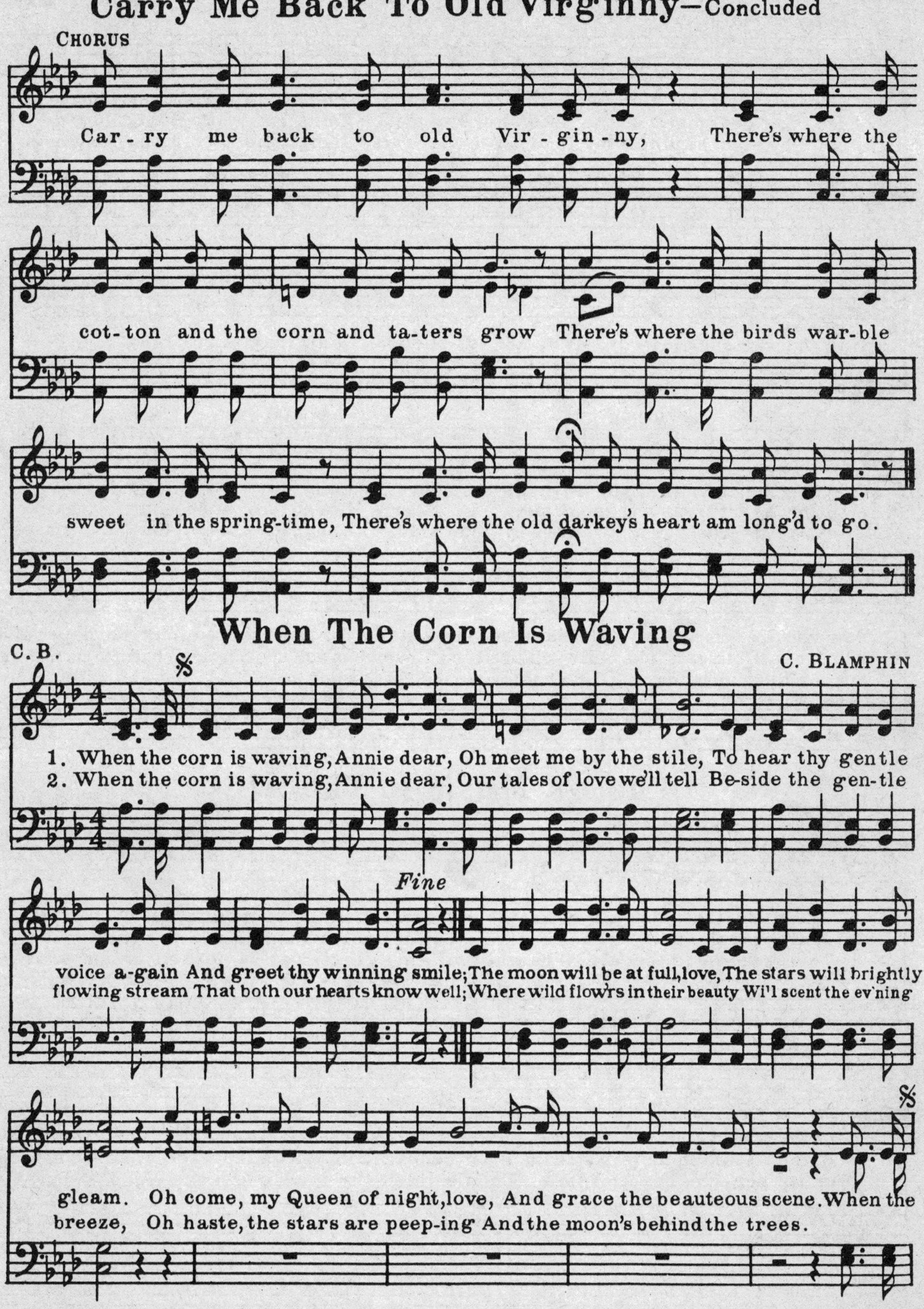
Carry Me Back To Old Virginny—Concluded
CHORUS
Car-ry me back to old Vir-gin-ny, There's where the
cot-ton and the corn and ta-ters grow There's where the birds war-ble
sweet in the spring-time, There's where the old darkey's heart am long'd to go.
When The Corn Is Waving
C. B.
C. BLAMPHIN
1. When the corn is waving, Annie dear, Oh meet me by the stile, To hear thy gentle
2. When the corn is waving, Annie dear, Our tales of love we'll tell Be-side the gen-tle
Fine
voice a-gain And greet thy winning smile; The moon will be at full, love, The stars will brightly
flowing stream That both our hearts know well; Where wild flow'rs in their beauty Wi'l scent the ev'ning
gleam. Oh come, my Queen of night, love, And grace the beauteous scene. When the
breeze, Oh haste, the stars are peep-ing And the moon's behind the trees.

"Carry Me Back To Old Virginny" is a favorite number for male quartets. An excellent effect may be secured by disposing of the parts as follows: Have the second tenor or "lead" sing the soprano part of the chorus, one octave lower than here given; the first tenor takes the alto part, singing it in the register of the alto voice; the first bass or baritone should carry the first line in the bass clef and the second bass, the lower line.

The same disposition of voices will give another fine number for male quartets in the song "When The Corn Is Waving."

T. H. B.
Long, Long Ago
Thomas H. Bayly
Moderately
1. Tell me the tales that to me were so dear, Long, long a-go, Long, long a-go;
2. Do you re-mem-ber the path where we met, Long, long a-go, Long, long a-go?
3. Tho' by your kindness my fond hopes were rais'd, Long, long a-go, Long, long a-go,
Fine
Sing me the songs I de-light-ed to hear, Long, long a-go, long a - go.
Ah, yes, you told me you ne'er would for-get, Long, long a-go, long a - go.
You by more el - o-quent lips have been prais'd, Long, long a-go, long a - go.
D.S. Let me be-lieve that you love as you loved, Long, long a-go, long a - go.
D.S. Still my heart treasures the praises I heard, Long, long a-go, long a - go.
D.S. Blest as I was when I sat by your side, Long, long a-go, long a - go.
D.S.
Now you are come, all my grief is re-moved, Let me for-get that so long you have rov'd,
Then, to all oth-ers, my smile you preferr'd, Love, when you spoke, gave a charm to each word,
But by long absence your truth has been tried, Still to your ac-cents I list - en with pride,
G.F.R.
There's Music In The Air
George F. Root
Moderately quick motion
1. There's mu-sic in the air When the in-fant morn is nigh, And faint its blush is seen
2. There's mu-sic in the air When the noontide's sultry beam Reflects a golden light
3. There's mu-sic in the air When the twilight's gentle sigh Is lost on evening's breast,
On the bright and laughing sky. Many a harp's ec - stat - ic sound, With its thrill of
On the distant mountain stream. When beneath some grateful shade, Sorrow's aching
As its pen-sive beauties die. Then, oh, then the loved ones gone Wake the pure ce-
joy pro-found, While we list, en-chant-ed there, To the mu-sic in the air.
head is laid, Sweet-ly to the spir - it there Comes the music in the air.
les-tial song, An-gel voi-ces greet us there, In the mu-sic in the air.

Flow Gently, Sweet Afton
ROBERT BURNS
JAMES E. SPILMAN
Not too slowly
1. Flow gen-tly, sweet Af-ton, a-mang thy green braes; Flow gently, I'll sing thee a
2. How loft-y, sweet Af-ton, thy neighboring hills, Far mark'd with the courses of
3. Thy crys-tal stream, Afton, how love-ly it glides, And winds by the cot where my
song in thy praise; My Ma-ry's a-sleep by thy murmuring stream, Flow gently, sweet
clear winding rills! There daily I wan-der, as morn ris-es high, My flocks and my
Ma - ry re-sides! How wanton thy wa-ters her snowy feet lave, As, gath'ring sweet
Af-ton, dis-turb not her dream. Thou stock-dove, whose ech-o re-sounds from the
Ma-ry's sweet cot in my eye. How pleas-ant thy banks and green val-leys be-
flow'rets, she stems thy clear wave! Flow gen-tly, sweet Af-ton, a-mang thy green
hill, Ye wild whistling black-birds in yon thorn-y dell, Thou green crest-ed
low, Where wild in the wood-lands the prim-ros-es blow! There oft, as mild
braes, Flow gen-tly, sweet riv-er, the theme of my lays: My Ma-ry's a
lap-wing, thy screaming for-bear, I charge you, dis-turb not my slum-ber-ing fair.
evening creeps o-ver the lea, The sweet scented birk shades my Ma-ry and me.
sleep by thy murmuring stream, Flow gen-tly, sweet Af-ton, dis-turb not her dream.

Loch Lomond

UNKNOWN
OLD SCOTCH AIR
1. By yon bonnie banks, And by yon bonnie braes, Where the sun shines bright on Loch Lo - mond, Where me and my true love Were ev - er wont to gae, On the bonnie, bonnie banks of Loch Lo - mond.
2. 'Twas then that we part-ed In yon shad-y glen, On the steep, steep side of Ben Lo - mond, Where in pur-ple hue The Highland hills we view, And the moon coming out in the gloam-ing.
3. The wee bir-dies sing, And the wild flowers spring, And in sunshine the waters are sleep - ing, But the broken heart it kens Nae second spring a-gain, Tho' the wae-ful may cease frae their greet - ing.
Brisker
CHORUS
Oh! ye'll take the high road, and I'll take the low road, And I'll be in Scot-land a - fore ye, But me and my true love we'll nev-er meet a - gain On the bonnie, bon-nie banks of Loch Lo - mond.
Scotland's Burning
(Round)
1 2 3 4
Scotlands burning, Scotland's burning, Look out, look out! Fire, fire, fire, fire! Pour on water, Pour on water.

Auld Lang Syne

ROBERT BURNS
SCOTCH AIR
1. Should auld acquaintance be for-got, And nev-er bro't to mind? Should auld acquaintance
2. And here's a hand, my trust-y frien', And gie's a hand o' thine; We'll tak' a cup o'
REFRAIN
be for-got, And days of auld lang syne?
kind-ness yet, For auld lang syne.
For auld lang syne, my dear, For
auld lang syne; We'll tak' a cup o' kind-ness yet For auld lang syne.
Comin' Thro' The Rye
ROBERT BURNS
SCOTCH AIR
Lively
1. If a bod-y meet a bod-y, Com-in' thro' the Rye, If a bod-y
2. If a bod-y meet a bod-y, Com-in' frae the town, If a bod-y
3. A-mang the train there is a swain I dear-ly love my-sel'; But what's his name, or
kiss a bod-y, Need a bod-y cry?
greet a bod-y, Need a bod-y frown?
where's his hame, I din-na choose to tell.
Ev-'ry las-sie has her lad-die,
Nane, they say, ha'e I; Yet a' the lads they smile on me,
When comin' thro' the Rye.

The Blue-Bells Of Scotland

ANNIE MC VICAR — OLD SCOTCH AIR

Moderately
1. O where, and O where is your High-land lad-die gone? O where, and O
2. O where, and O where does your High-land lad-die dwell? O where, and O
3 Sup-pose, and sup-pose that your High-land lad should die? Sup-pose, and sup-
cresc.
where is your Highland lad-die gone? He's gone to fight the foe for King
where does your Highland lad-die dwell? He dwelt in mer-ry Scot-land, at the
pose that your Highland lad should die? The bag-pipes shall play o'er him, and I'd
George up-on the throne; And it's oh! in my heart, how I wish him safe at home!
sign of the Blue-Bell; And it's oh! in my heart that I love my lad-die well.
lay me down and cry; But it's oh! in my heart that I wish he may not die.
Oh, Wert Thou In The Cauld Blast
ROBERT BURNS
FELIX MENDELSSOHN
1. Oh, wert thou in the cauld blast, On yon-der lea, On yon-der lea, My plaidie to the angry
2. Oh, were I in the wildest waste, Sae bleak and bare, Sae bleak and bare, The desert were a Para-
airt, I'd shel-ter thee, I'd shel-ter thee; Or did mis-for-tune's bit-ter storms A-
dise If thou wert there, If thou wert there; Or were I mon-arch of the globe, With
round thee blaw, A-round thee blaw, Thy shield should be my bosom, To share it a', To share it a'.
thee to reign, With thee to reign, The brightest jewel in my crown Wad be my queen, Wad be my queen.

Annie Laurie
William Douglass
Lady John Scott
Moderately quick
1. Max-wel-ton's braes are bon-nie, Where ear - ly fa's the dew, And 'twas
2. Her brow is like the snow-drift, Her throat is like the swan; Her
3. Like dew on th' gow-an ly-ing Is th' fa' o'her fair-y feet, And like
there that Annie Lau-rie Gave me her prom-ise true; Gave me her prom-ise true,
face it is the fair-est That e'er the sun shone on; That e'er the sun shone on,
winds in summer sighing, Her voice is low and sweet; Her voice is low and sweet,
Which ne'er forgot will be, And for bon-nie An-nie Lau-rie, I'd lay me doon and dee.
And dark blue is her e'e, And for bon-nie An-nie Lau-rie, I'd lay me doon and dee.
And she's a' the world to me, And for bon-nie An-nie Lau-rie, I'd lay me doon and dee.
Robin Adair
Caroline Keppel
Scotch Air
1. What's this dull town to me? Ro-bin's not near; What was't I wished to see, What wish'd to hear? Where's all the joy and mirth
2. What made th' as-sem-bly shine? Ro-bin A - dair; What made the ball so fine? Ro bin was there; What, when the play was o'er,
3. But now thou'rt cold to me, Ro-bin A - dair; But now thou'rt cold to me, Ro-bin A - dair; Yet, him I loved so well,
That made this town a heav'n on earth? Oh! they're all fled with thee, Ro-bin A - dair.
What made my heart so sore? Oh! it was part-ing with Ro-bin A - dair.
Still in my heart shall dwell, Oh! I can ne'er for-get Ro-bin A - dair.

Hail To The Chief

SIR WALTER SCOTT | JAMES SANDERSON

1. Hail to the chief, who in triumph ad-van-ces, Hon-ored and bless'd be the ev-ergreen pine!
2. Ours is no sapling, chance-sown by the fountain, Blooming at Beltane, in winter to fade; When the
3. Row vassals, row for the pride of the Highlands! Stretch to your oars for the evergreen pine!

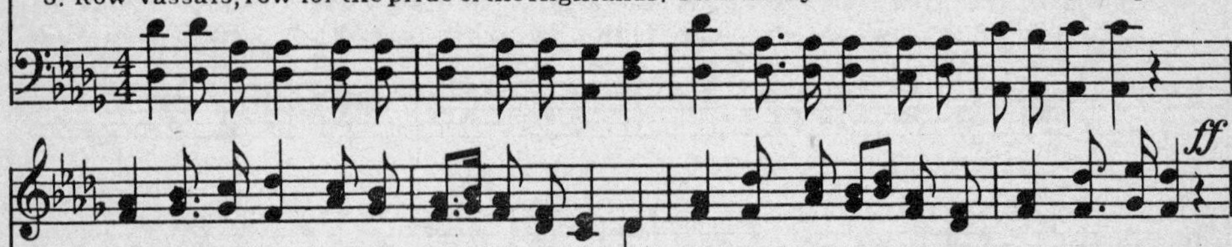

Long may the tree in his banner that glances, Flourish, the shelter and grace of our line.
whirl-wind has stripp'd ev'ry leaf on the mountain, The more shall Clan-Alpine exult in her shade.
Oh, that the rosebud that graces yon islands, Were wreath'd in a garland around him to twine!

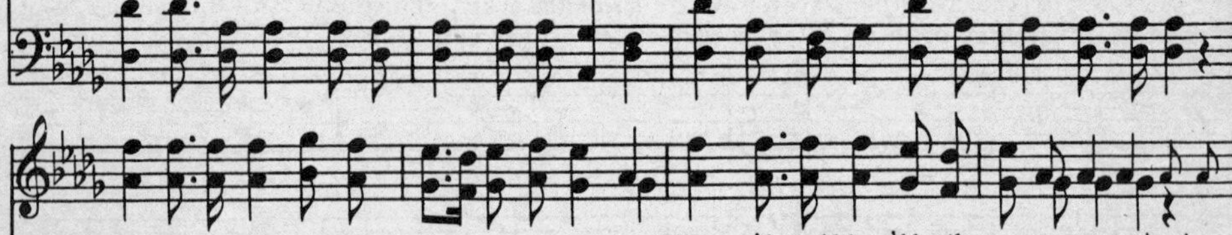

Hail to the chief, who in triumph ad-van-ces, Hon-or'd and bless'd be the ev-er-green pine!
Ours is no sapling, chance-sown by the fountain, Blooming at Beltane, in winter to fade; When the
Row, vassals, row, for the pride of the Highlands! Stretch to your oars for the evergreen pine!

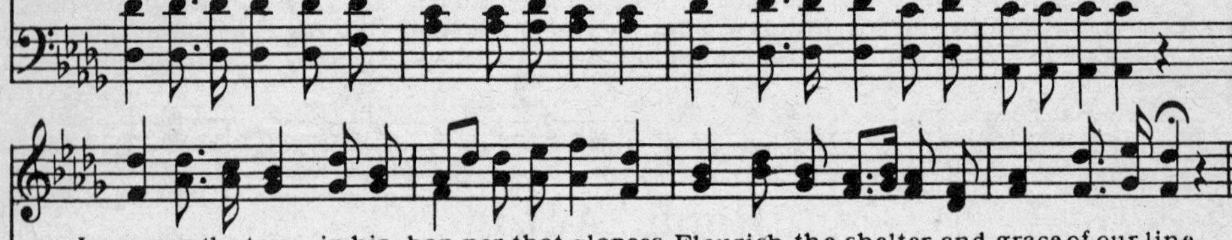

Long may the tree in his ban-ner that glances, Flourish, the shelter and grace of our line.
whirl-wind has stripp'd ev'ry leaf on the mountain, The more shall Clan-Alpine exult in her shade.
Oh, that the rose-bud that graces yon islands, Were wreath'd in a garland around him to twine!

Heav'n send it hap-py dew, Earth lend it sap a-new; Gai-ly to bourgeon and broadly to grow;
Moor'd in the rift-ed rock, Proof to the tempest shock, Firmer he roots him, the ruder it blow;
O, that some seedling gem, Worthy such noble stem, Honor'd and bless'd in their shadow might grow!

While ev-'ry highland glen, Sends our shout back again, "Roderigh Vich Alpine dhu, ho! i-e-roe!"
Menteith and Breadalbane, then, Echo his praise a-gain, "Roderigh Vich Alpine dhu, ho! i-e-roe!"
Loud should Clan-Alpine then, Ring from her deepmost glen, "Roderigh Vich Alpine dhu, ho! i-e-roe!"

The Last Rose Of Summer

Thomas Moore, the great Irish lyric poet, did for Irish folk songs what Burns did for those of his native land. "The Last Rose of Summer" is among his most famous songs, having achieved great popularity through its interpolation into the ever popular and beautiful opera "Martha" by Flotow, to whom the authorship of the song is sometimes erroneously attributed. The air is an ancient one, called the "Groves of Blarney," which in turn was taken from a more ancient Celtic melody.

THOMAS MOORE
IRISH AIR
1. 'Tis the last rose of summer, Left blooming a - lone;
All her love-ly companions Are fad - ed and gone;
No flower of her kindred
2. I'll not leave thee, thou lone one, To pine on the stem;
Since the love-ly are sleeping, Go sleep thou with them;
Thus kind-ly I scatter
3. So soon may I fol - low, When friend-ships de-cay,
And from love's shining cir-cle The gems drop a - way;
When true hearts lie withered
rit.
No rose-bud is nigh, To re-flect back her blushes, Or give sigh for sigh.
Thy leaves o'er the bed Where thy mates of the garden Lie scent - less and dead.
And fond ones have flown, Oh, who would in - hab-it This bleak world a - lone.
Attributed to
H. BOULTON
All Through The Night
OLD WELSH AIR
Softly
1. Sleep, my child, and peace at-tend thee All thro' the night; Guardian an-gels
2. While the moon her watch is keep-ing All thro' the night; While the wea-ry
God will send thee, All thro' the night, Soft the drow-sy hours are creeping
world is sleep-ing All thro' the night. O'er thy spir - it gen - tly steal-ing,
Hill and vale in slum-ber steeping, I my loving vig - il keeping All thro' the night.
Visions of de-light re-veal-ing, Breathes a pure and ho-ly feeling, All thro' the night.

Sweet and Low

ALFRED TENNYSON | JOSEPH BARNBY

pp Slowly
1. Sweet and low, sweet and low, Wind of the west - ern sea;
2. Sleep and rest, sleep and rest, Fa - ther will come to thee soon;
sf
p
Low, low, breathe and blow, Wind of the west - ern sea;
Rest, rest, on moth - er's breast, Fa - ther will come to thee soon;
mf
pp
O - ver the roll - ing wa - ters go, Come from the
O - - ver the wa - ters go, Come
Fa - ther will come to his babe in the nest, Sil - ver
Fa - - ther will come to his babe, Sil - ver
f
dy - ing moon and blow, Blow him a - gain to me,
from the moon and blow,
sails all out of the west, Un - der the sil - ver moon,
sails out of the west,
p
rall e dim.
pp
While my lit - tle one, while my pret - ty one, sleeps.
Sleep, my lit - tle one, sleep, my pret - ty one, sleep.

M. W. B.

Killarney

MICHAEL W. BALFE

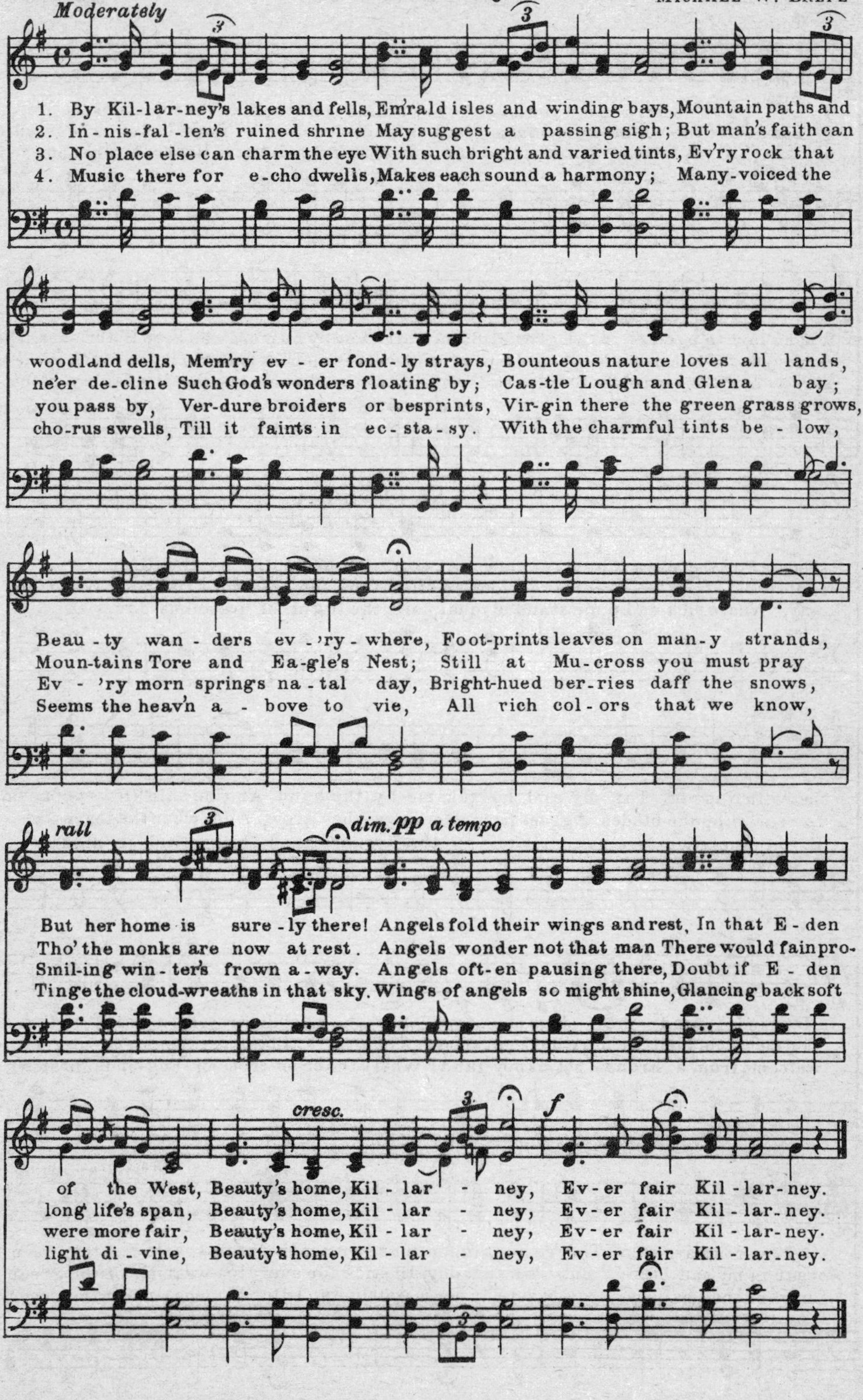

Moderately

1. By Kil-lar-ney's lakes and fells, Em'rald isles and winding bays, Mountain paths and
2. In-nis-fal-len's ruined shrine May suggest a passing sigh; But man's faith can
3. No place else can charm the eye With such bright and varied tints, Ev'ry rock that
4. Music there for e-cho dwells, Makes each sound a harmony; Many-voiced the

woodland dells, Mem'ry ev - er fond-ly strays, Bounteous nature loves all lands,
ne'er de-cline Such God's wonders floating by; Cas-tle Lough and Glena bay;
you pass by, Ver-dure broiders or besprints, Vir-gin there the green grass grows,
cho-rus swells, Till it faints in ec-sta-sy. With the charmful tints be - low,

Beau - ty wan - ders ev - 'ry - where, Foot-prints leaves on man-y strands,
Moun-tains Tore and Ea-gle's Nest; Still at Mu-cross you must pray
Ev - 'ry morn springs na - tal day, Bright-hued ber-ries daff the snows,
Seems the heav'n a - bove to vie, All rich col-ors that we know,

rall *dim.* *pp* *a tempo*

But her home is sure - ly there! Angels fold their wings and rest, In that E-den
Tho' the monks are now at rest. Angels wonder not that man There would fain pro-
Smil-ing win-ter's frown a-way. Angels oft-en pausing there, Doubt if E-den
Tinge the cloud-wreaths in that sky. Wings of angels so might shine, Glancing back soft

cresc. *f*

of the West, Beauty's home, Kil - lar - ney, Ev-er fair Kil-lar-ney.
long life's span, Beauty's home, Kil - lar - ney, Ev-er fair Kil-lar-ney.
were more fair, Beauty's home, Kil - lar - ney, Ev-er fair Kil-lar-ney.
light di-vine, Beauty's home, Kil - lar - ney, Ev-er fair Kil-lar-ney.

Wearing Of The Green

DION BOUCICAULT

IRISH AIR

Moderately

1. Oh! Pad-dy, dear, and did you hear the news that's going round, The shamrock is for -
2. Then since the col-or we must wear, is England's cruel red, Sure Ireland's sons will
3. But if at last our col-or should be torn from Ireland's heart, Her sons with shame and

bid by law to grow on I-rish ground; Saint Patrick's day no more we'll keep, His color can't be
ne'er forget the blood that they have shed; You may take the shamrock from your hat, and cast it on the
sorrow from the dear old soil will part; I've heard whisper of a country that lies far beyant the

seen, For there's a blood-y law a-gin' the Wear-in' o' the Green; I
sod, But 'twill take root and flourish still, tho un-der-foot 'tis trod; When the
say, Where rich and poor stand e-qual, in the light of freedom's day; Oh,

met with Nap-per Tan-dy and he tuk me by the hand, And he said "How's poor ould
law can stop the blades of grass from growing as they grow, And when the leaves in
E - rin must we lave you, driv-en by the tyrant's hand, Must we ask a moth-er's

Ire-land, and how does she stand?" She's the most dis-tressful country, that
sum-mer time their verdure dare not show; Then I will change the col-or I
welcome from a strange but happy land? Where the cruel cross of England's thraldom

Repeat as Chorus

ev-er you have seen; They're hanging men and women there for wearing of the green.
wear in my cau-been, But 'till that day, I'll stick for aye to wearing of the green.
nev-er shall be seen, And where, in peace, we'll live and die, a - wearing of the green.

Believe Me, If All Those Endearing Young Charms—Conc.

fair - y gifts, fad - ing a - way, Thou wouldst still be a - dored — as this
time will but make thee more dear! No, the heart that has tru - ly loved
moment thou art, Let thy love - li - ness fade as it will; And a - round the dear
nev - er for - gets, But as tru - ly loves on to the close; As the sun - flow - er
ru - in, each wish of my heart Would en - twine it - self ver - dant - ly still!
turns on her god, when he sets, The same look which she turn'd when he rose!
The Harp That Once Through Tara's Halls
THOMAS MOORE
SIR JOHN STEVENSON
1. The harp that once thro' Tara's halls The soul of music shed; Now hangs as mute on
2. No more to chiefs and ladies bright The harp of Tara swells; The chord a - lone that
Ta - ra's walls As tho' that soul were fled. So sleeps the pride of former days, So
breaks at night Its tale of ru - in tells. Thus Freedom now so seldom wakes; The
glo - ry's thrill is o'er, And hearts that once beat high for praise Now feel that pulse no more.
on - ly throb she gives Is when some heart, in - dignant, breaks, To show that still she lives.

Kathleen Mavourneen

Mrs. JULIA CRAWFORD

FREDERICK N CROUCH

Moderately quick

mf mf mf

1. Kathleen Ma-vourneen, the gray dawn is breaking, The horn of the hun-ter is
2. Kathleen Ma-vourneen, a - wake from thy slumbers; The blue mountains glow in the

Small notes to be sung for 2d V.

mf

heard on the hill; The lark from her light wing the bright dew is shak - ing;
sun's golden light; Ah! where is the spell that once hung on my numbers? A -

Kathleen Mavour-neen, what! slumb'ring still? Kathleen Mavourneen, what!
rise in thy beauty, thou star of my night; A - rise in thy beau-ty, thou

f

slum - b'ring still? Or hast thou for-got-ten how soon we must sev-er? Oh!
star of my night! Ma-vour-neen, Ma-vour-neen, my sad tears are falling, To

mf fz mf

hast thou for-gotten this day we must part?
think that from E-rin and thee I must part!
It may be for years, and it

mf *semplice* mf

may be for ev-er; Then why art thou si-lent, thou voice of my heart? It may be for

When you realize that the songs in this book, if bought separately in sheet form, would cost you from ten to fifty cents each and that you get all of them for but a few cents, you know it's mighty big value. Why not tell others about it?

Kathleen Mavourneen—Continued

years, and it may be for ev er; Then why art thou si-lent, Kathleen Ma-vourneen?
The Heart Bowed Down
M.W.B.
(From "The Bohemian Girl")
MICHAEL Wm. BALFE
Moderately slow
1. The heart bow'd down by weight of woe, To weak-est hopes will cling, To thought and im-pulse while they flow, That can no com - fort bring, that can, that can no com - fort bring; To those ex-cit-ing scenes will blend, O'er pleasure's pathway thrown; But mem'ry is the on - ly friend That grief can call its own, That grief can call its own, That grief can call its own
2. The mind will in its worst de-spair, Still pon-der o'er the past, On mo - ments of de - light that were Too beauti-ful to last, that were too beau-ti - ful to last; To long de-part-ed years ex-tend, Its vi-sions with them flown; For mem'ry is the on - ly friend That grief can call its

When You And I Were Young, Maggie

GEORGE W. JOHNSON J. A. BUTTERFIELD

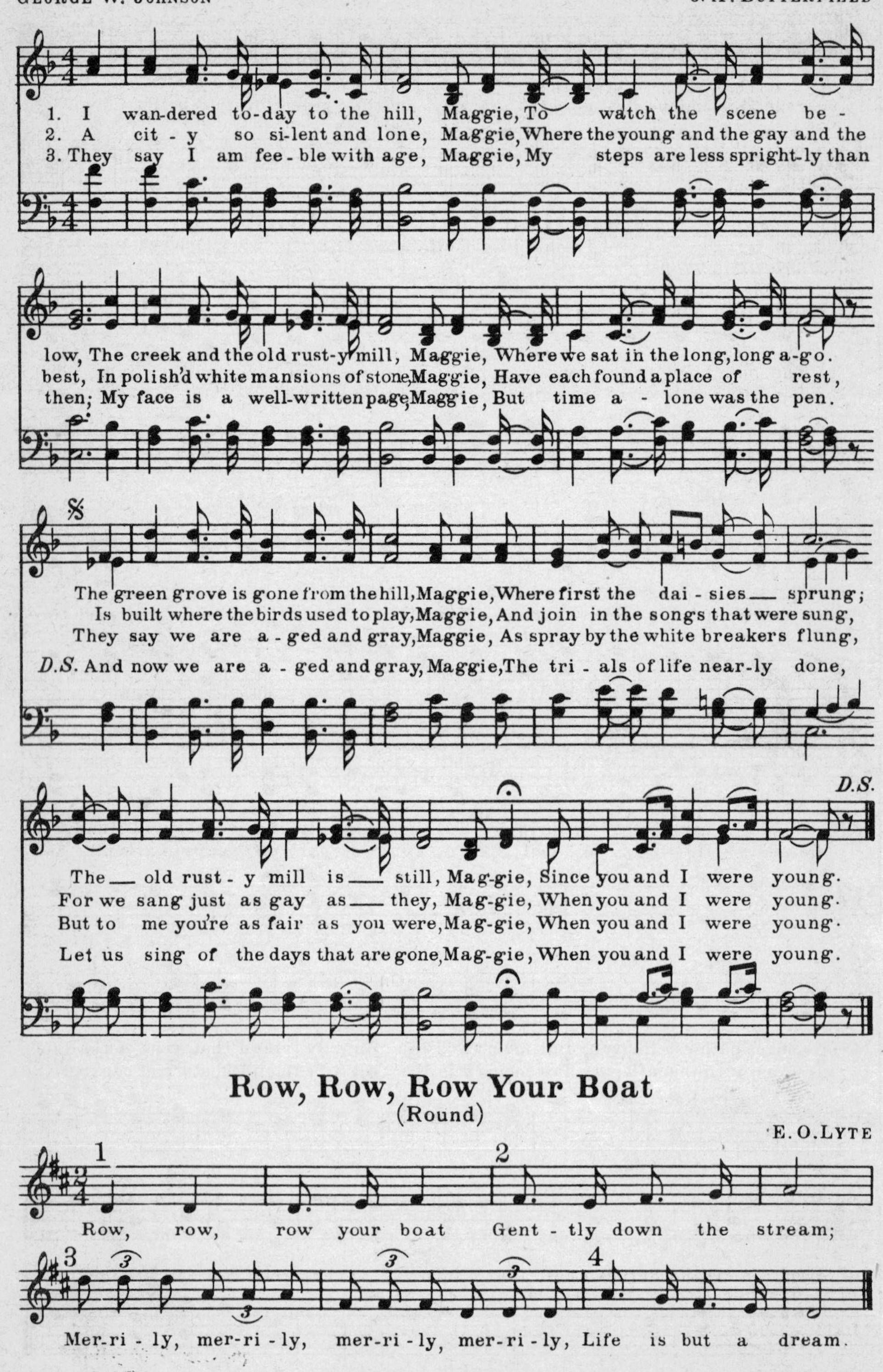
1. I wan-dered to-day to the hill, Maggie, To watch the scene be -
2. A cit - y so si-lent and lone, Maggie, Where the young and the gay and the
3. They say I am fee - ble with age, Maggie, My steps are less spright-ly than
low, The creek and the old rust-y mill, Maggie, Where we sat in the long, long a-go.
best, In polish'd white mansions of stone, Maggie, Have each found a place of rest,
then; My face is a well-written page, Maggie, But time a - lone was the pen.
The green grove is gone from the hill, Maggie, Where first the dai - sies — sprung;
Is built where the birds used to play, Maggie, And join in the songs that were sung,
They say we are a - ged and gray, Maggie, As spray by the white breakers flung,
D.S. And now we are a - ged and gray, Maggie, The tri - als of life near-ly done,
D.S.
The — old rust - y mill is — still, Mag-gie, Since you and I were young.
For we sang just as gay as — they, Mag-gie, When you and I were young.
But to me you're as fair as you were, Mag-gie, When you and I were young.
Let us sing of the days that are gone, Mag-gie, When you and I were young.
Row, Row, Row Your Boat
(Round)
E. O. LYTE
1 2
Row, row, row your boat Gent - tly down the stream;
3 4
Mer-ri - ly, mer-ri - ly, mer-ri - ly, mer-ri - ly, Life is but a dream.

THOMAS MOORE
The Minstrel Boy
IRISH AIR
Lively
1. The min - strel boy to the war is gone, In the ranks of death you'll find him; His fa - ther's sword he hath gird - ed on, And his wild harp slung be - hind him.
2. The min - strel fell, but the foe - man's chain Could not bring that proud soul un - der; The harp he lov'd ne'er spoke a - gain, For he tore its chords a - sun - der, And
"Land of song!" said the war - rior bard, "Tho' all the world be - trays thee, One sword at least thy rights shall guard, One faith-ful harp shall praise thee."
said, "No chain shall sul - ly thee, Thou soul of love and brav - 'ry! Thy songs were made for the pure and free, They shall nev - er sound in slav - 'ry."

Moore, Jonson and Burns

Thomas Moore, the great Irish poet, was born in Dublin in 1779 and died in 1852. As a song writer, Moore is one of the greatest; he is excellent alike in verse, romance and satire.

Ben Jonson, (1573 - 1637), famous among English dramatists and poets, is noted for his charmingly beautiful work. His poems are many and varied; they are full of grace and are classical in form and phraseology. After three centuries his, "Drink To Me Only With Thine Eyes," which is on page 46 is still popular.

Robert Burns, the national poet of Scotland was born in a little clay cottage near Ayr in 1759. At the time of his death in 1796 he was recognized for his great genius but he died in penury. It was his custom to write his poems to existing Scotch airs and to this habit we owe some of the greatest lyrics in the language.

Juanita

"Juanita," for many years a favorite, was written by the granddaughter of Richard Brinsley Sheridan, the Irish wit and playwright. The Honorable Mrs. Norton, as she was called, adapted her text to an old Spanish air, and rearranged it much in its present form.

Mrs. CAROLINE NORTON
SPANISH AIR
1. Soft o'er the foun-tain, lin-g'ring falls the southern moon; Far o'er the mountain,
2. When in thy dream ing Moons like these shall shine again, And daylight beaming,
Breaks the day too soon! In thy dark eyes, splendor, Where the warm light loves to dwell,
Prove thy dreams are vain, Wilt thou not, re lent ing, For thine absent lov er sigh?
Wear-y looks, yet ten-der, Speak their fond fare-well. Ni ta! Jua ni ta!
In thy heart con sent ing To a pray'r gone by? Ni ta! Jua ni ta!
Ask thy soul if we should part! Ni-ta! Jua - ni-ta! Lean thou on my heart.
Let me lin-ger by thy side! Ni-ta! Jua - ni-ta! Be my own Fair Bride.
The Dearest Spot
W. T. W.
W. T. WRIGHTON
1. The dear-est spot on earth to me Is home, sweet home; The fair - y land I've
2. I've taught my heart the way to prize My home, sweet home; I've learn'd to look with
D.C. The dear-est spot on earth to me Is home, sweet home; The fair - y land I've
Fine.
long'd to see Is home, sweet home; There how charm'd the sense of hearing, There where hearts are
lover's eyes On home, sweet home; There where vows are tru - ly plighted, There where hearts are
long'd to see Is home, sweet home.

The Dearest Spot— Continued

D.C.
so en-dear-ing; All the world is not so cheer-ing As home, sweet home.
so u - ni - ted; All the world be-sides I've slighted For home, sweet home.
Rocked In The Cradle Of The Deep
EMMA WILLARD
JOSEPH P. KNIGHT
1. Rocked in the cra-dle of the deep, I lay me down in peace to sleep;
2. And such the trust that still were mine, Tho' stormy winds sweep o'er the brine,
Se-cure I rest up-on the wave, For Thou, O Lord, hast pow'r to save.
Or though the tempest's fier-y breath Rouse me from sleep to wreck and death,
I know Thou wilt not slight my call, For Thou dost mark the sparrow's fall;
In o-cean cave still safe with Thee, The germ of im-mor-tal-i-ty;
And calm and peace-ful is my sleep, Rocked in the cra-dle of the deep;
And calm and peace-ful is my sleep, Rocked in the cra-dle of the deep.

Largo
Thomas Williams
(From the Opera, Xerxes)
George Friedrich Handel
Very slowly
p
Fa - - ther in heav'n, Thy chil-dren hear, As they a -
dor-ing bow, O Thou Al-might-y One, Hear Thou, our pray'r; Strengthen our
mf
p
faith; With hope in - spire our hearts, Flaming our souls with love
f
3

Largo - Continued
pp
Like un - to Thine. Then ___ shall Thy works a-bound, Men shall pro -
pp
f
claim that God our Lord ___ is God a-lone, And ho - ly,
f
p
3
ho - ly is His name, ___ And ho - ly is His name;
p
ff
God our Lord is God a-lone, And ho - ly, ho-ly is His name.
ff
God our Lord is God a-lone, And ho - ly, ho-ly is His name.
ff
ff
8

Holy, Holy, Holy
Reginald Heber
John B. Dykes
1. Ho-ly, ho-ly, ho-ly! Lord God Al-migh-ty! Ear-ly in the
2. Ho-ly, ho-ly, ho-ly! all the saints a-dore Thee, Cast-ing down their
3. Ho-ly, ho-ly, ho-ly! though the dark-ness hide Thee, Though the eye of
4. Ho-ly, ho-ly, ho-ly! Lord God Al-migh-ty! All Thy works shall
morn-ing our song shall rise to Thee. Ho-ly, ho-ly, ho-ly,
golden crowns a-round the glas-sy sea; Cher-u-bim and Sera-phim
sin-ful man Thy glo-ry may not see, On-ly Thou art ho-ly!
praise Thy name in earth, and sky, and sea. Ho-ly, ho-ly, ho-ly!
mer-ci-ful and migh-ty, God in three per-sons, bless-ed Trin-i-ty!
fall-ing down be-fore Thee, Which wert, and art, and ev-er-more shalt be.
there is none be-side Thee, Per-fect in pow'r, in love, and pu-ri-ty.
mer-ci-ful and migh-ty, God in three per-sons, bless-ed Trin-i-ty!
Come, Thou Almighty King
(Italian Hymn)
Charles Wesley
Giardini
1. Come, Thou al-might-y King, Help us Thy name to sing, Help us to praise! Fa-ther all-
2. Come, Thou in-car-nate Word, Gird on Thy might-y sword, Our pray'r attend! Come, and Thy
3. Come, Ho-ly Com-fort-er, Thy sacred wit-ness bear, In this glad hour! Thou, who al-
glo-ri-ous, O'er all vic-to-ri-ous, Come and reign o-ver us, An-cient of days!
peo-ple bless, And give Thy word success: Spir-it of ho-li-ness, On us de-scend!
might-y art, Now rule in ev'ry heart, And ne'er from us depart, Spir-it of pow'r!

Onward, Christian Soldiers

In 1865, the Rev. Sabine Baring-Gould was Curate of the Horbury Bridge School in a small English village. A school festival was to be given for which a suitable song was desired but he could find no song in his books which he considered suitable to the occasion. To supply the necessity he wrote this now famous processional hymn which is the most universally sung of the hymns of today.

The spirited music written for it by Sir Arthur Seymour Sullivan has doubtless added to the enthusiasm with which it is always sung.

SABINE BARING-GOULD
SIR ARTHUR SEYMOUR SULLIVAN
1. On-ward, Christian sol-diers! Marching as to war, With the cross of Je-sus
2. Like a might-y ar-my Moves the Church of God; Brothers, we are tread-ing
3. Crowns and thrones may perish, Kingdoms rise and wane, But the Church of Je-sus
4. On-ward, then, ye peo-ple! Join our hap-py throng, Blend with ours your voices
Go-ing on be-fore: Christ, the roy-al Mas-ter, Leads a-gainst the foe;
Where the saints have trod; We are not di-vid-ed, All one bod-y we,
Con-stant will re-main; Gates of hell can nev-er 'Gainst that Church pre-vail;
In the tri-umph-song; Glo-ry, laud, and hon-or Un-to Christ the King.
For-ward in-to bat-tle, See, His ban-ners go!
One in hope and doc-trine One in char-i-ty.
We have Christ's own promise, And that can-not fail.
This thro' countless a-ges Men and an-gels sing.
CHORUS
Onward, Christian soldiers!
Marching as to war,
With the cross of Je-sus Go-ing on be-fore.
Now the Day Is Over
SABINE BARING-GOULD
JOSEPH BARNBY
1. Now the day is o-ver, Night is drawing nigh, Shadows of the ev'ning Steal across the sky.
2. Jesus, give the weary Calm and sweet repose, With Thy tend'rest blessing, May our eyelids close.
3. When the morning wakens, Then may we arise Pure and fresh and sinless In Thy holy eyes.

Work, For The Night Is Coming
ANNIE L. WALKER-COGHILL
LOWELL MASON
1.Work, for the night is com - ing, Work thro' the morn-ing hours;
2.Work, for the night is com - ing, Work thro' the sun - ny noon;
3.Work, for the night is com - ing, Un - der the sun - set skies;
Fine.
Work, while the dew is spark - ling, Work 'mid spring-ing flow'rs;
Fill bright - est hours with la - bor, Rest comes sure and soon.
While their bright tints are glow - ing, Work, for day - light flies,
D.S. Work, for the night is com - ing, When man's work is done.
D.S. Work, for the night is com - ing, When man works no more.
D.S. Work while the night is dark'n - ing When man's work is o'er.
cresc.
D.S.
Work, when the day grows bright - er, Work in the glow-ing sun;
Give ev - 'ry fly - ing min - ute, Some-thing to keep in store;
Work till the last beam fad - eth, Fad - eth to shine no more;
Jesus, Tender Shepherd, Hear Me
CLARIBEL
Mrs. CHARLES BARNARD (CLARIBEL)
1. Je - sus, ten - der Shep-herd, hear me; Bless Thy lit - tle lamb to - night;
2. All this day Thy hand has led me, And I thank Thee for Thy care;
3. Let my sins be all for - giv - en; Bless the friends I love so well;
Thro' the dark-ness be Thou near me, Keep me safe till morn-ing light.
Thou hast clothed me, warmed and fed me, List - en to my eve - ning pray'r!
Take me, when I die, to heav - en, Hap - py there with Thee to dwell.

The Twenty-third Psalm

The Lord is my shepherd; I shall not want. He maketh me to lie down in green pastures: he leadeth me beside the still waters. He restoreth my soul: he leadeth me in the paths of righteousness for his name's sake. Yea, though I walk through the valley of the shadow of death, I will fear no evil, for thou art with me; thy rod and thy staff they comfort me. Thou preparest a table before me in the presence of mine enemies: thou anointest my head with oil; my cup runneth over. Surely goodness and mercy shall follow me all the days of my life; and I will dwell in the house of the Lord for ever.

My Faith Looks Up to Thee

RAY PALMER | LOWELL MASON

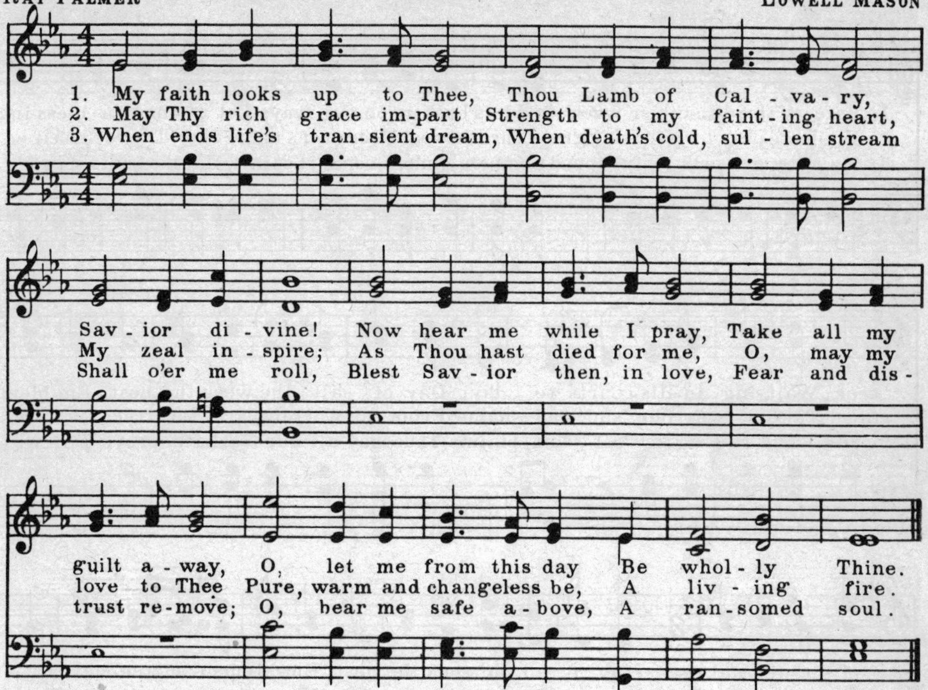

1. My faith looks up to Thee, Thou Lamb of Cal-va-ry,
2. May Thy rich grace im-part Strength to my faint-ing heart,
3. When ends life's tran-sient dream, When death's cold, sul-len stream

Sav-ior di-vine! Now hear me while I pray, Take all my
My zeal in-spire; As Thou hast died for me, O, may my
Shall o'er me roll, Blest Sav-ior then, in love, Fear and dis-

guilt a-way, O, let me from this day Be whol-ly Thine.
love to Thee Pure, warm and changeless be, A liv-ing fire.
trust re-move; O, bear me safe a-bove, A ran-somed soul.

Abide with Me

HENRY F. LYTE | WILLIAM H. MONK

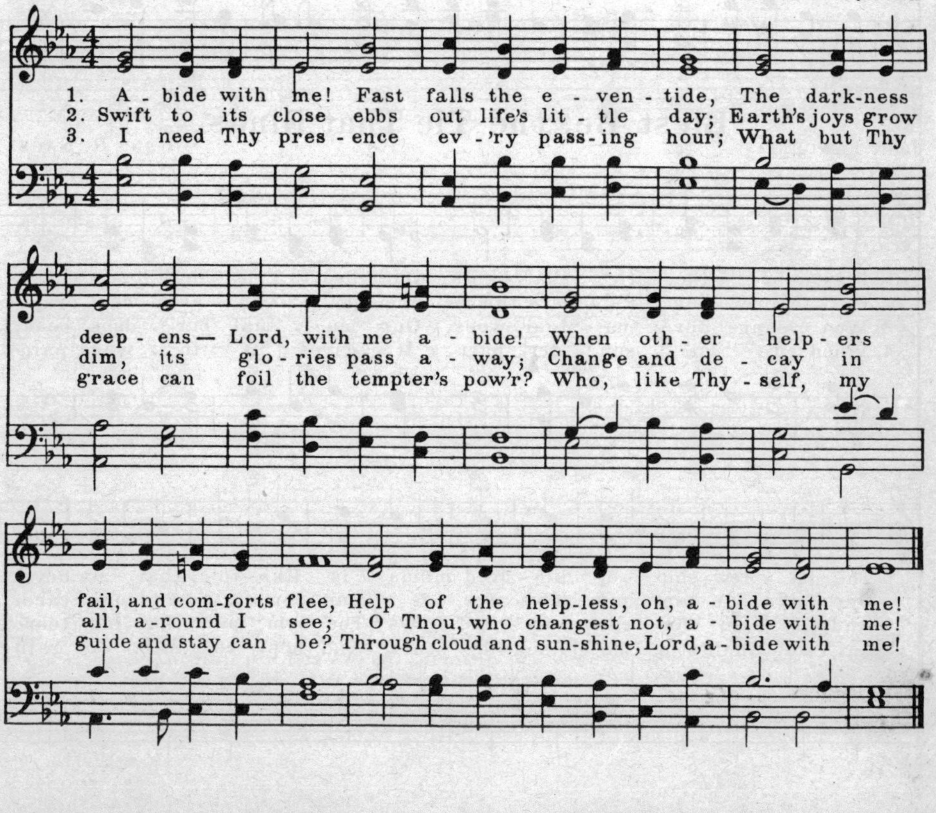

1. A-bide with me! Fast falls the e-ven-tide, The dark-ness
2. Swift to its close ebbs out life's lit-tle day; Earth's joys grow
3. I need Thy pres-ence ev-'ry pass-ing hour; What but Thy

deep-ens— Lord, with me a-bide! When oth-er help-ers
dim, its glo-ries pass a-way; Change and de-cay in
grace can foil the tempter's pow'r? Who, like Thy-self, my

fail, and com-forts flee, Help of the help-less, oh, a-bide with me!
all a-round I see; O Thou, who changest not, a-bide with me!
guide and stay can be? Through cloud and sun-shine, Lord, a-bide with me!

Safely Through Another Week

JOHN NEWTON — LOWELL MASON

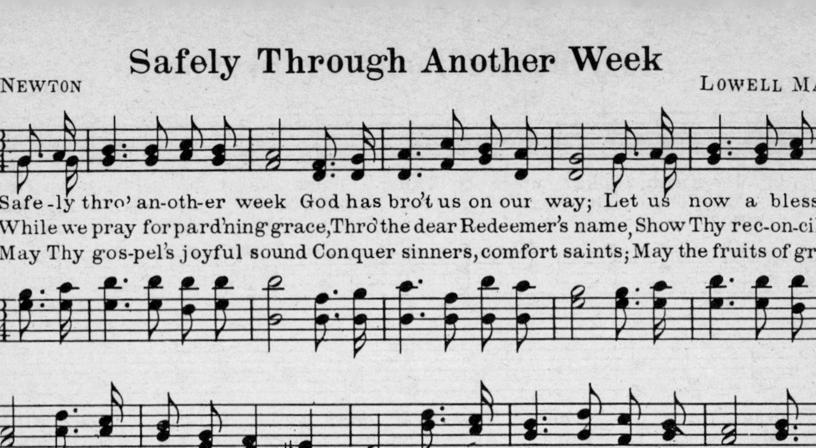
1. Safe-ly thro' an-oth-er week God has bro't us on our way; Let us now a bless-ing
2. While we pray for pard'ning grace, Thro' the dear Redeemer's name, Show Thy rec-on-cil-ed
3. May Thy gos-pel's joyful sound Conquer sinners, comfort saints; May the fruits of grace a-

seek, Wait-ing in His courts to - day; Day of all the week the best, Em-blem
face, Take a - way our sin and shame; From our worldly cares set free, May we
bound, Bring re-lief for all com-plaints: Thus may all our Sabbaths prove Till we

of e-ter-nal rest; Day of all the week the best, Em-blem of e-ter-nal rest.
rest this day in Thee; From our worldly cares set free, May we rest this day in Thee.
join the Church above; Thus may all our Sabbaths prove Till we join the Church a-bove.

Blest Be the Tie That Binds

JOHN FAWCETT — HANS G. NAGELI

1. Blest be the tie that binds Our hearts in Christ - ian love;
2. Be - fore our Fa - ther's throne, We pour our ar - dent pray'rs;
3. We share our mu - tual woes, Our mu - tual bur - dens bear;
4. When we a - sun - der part, It gives us in - ward pain;
The fel - low-ship of kin - dred minds Is like to that a - bove.
Our fears, our hopes, our aims are one, Our com-forts and our cares
And oft - en for each oth - er flows The sym - pa - thiz - ing tear.
But we shall still be joined in heart, And hope to meet a - gain.

Jesus, Lover of My Soul

In the foremost ranks of the composers of immortal lyric verse stands Charles Wesley. Several stories are told of the circumstances under which he wrote these beautiful stanzas but whatever the inciting cause, it resulted in inspiring one of the noblest songs of modern times. It is a song of comfort and of refuge, one that has brought peace and contentment to vast multitudes.

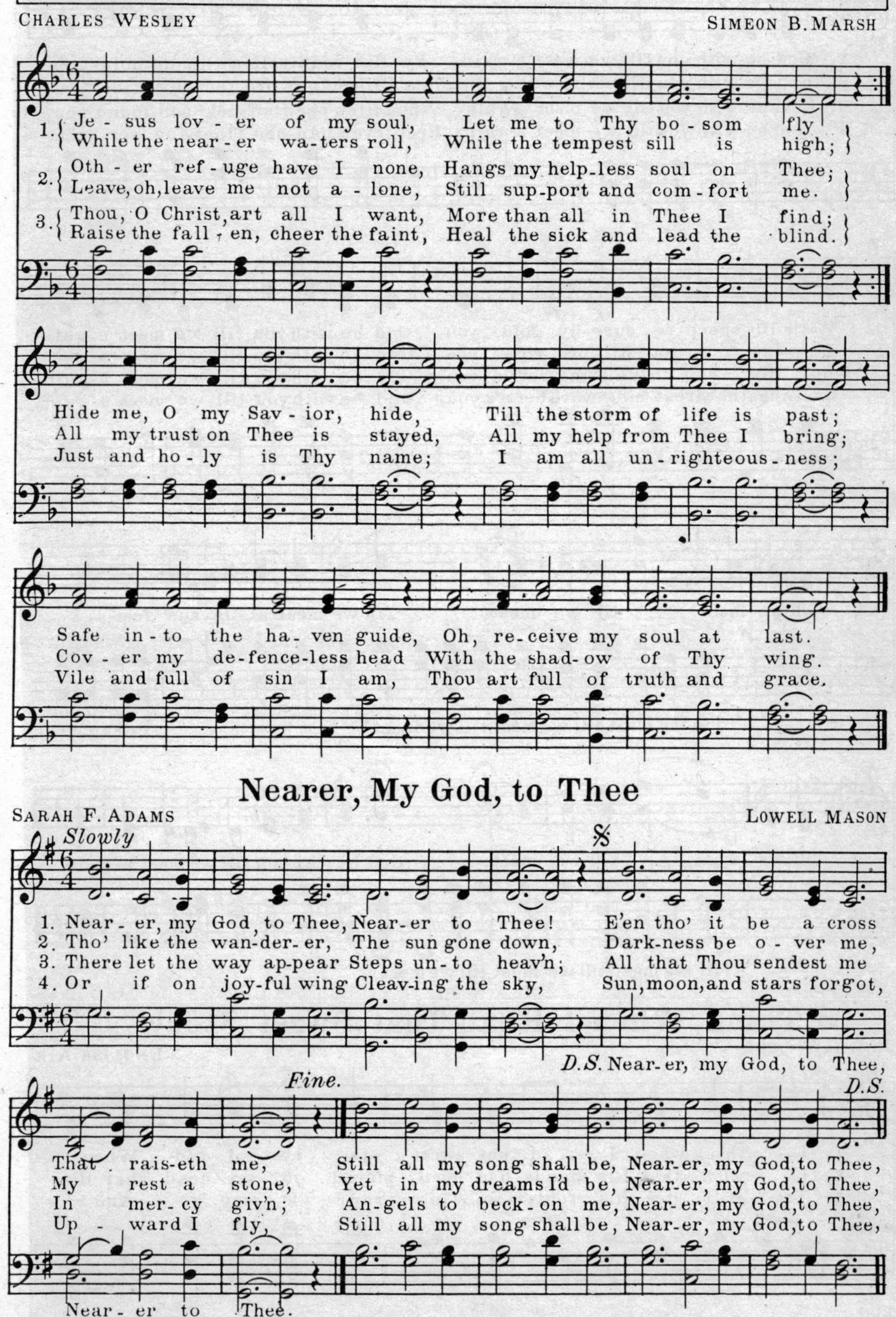
CHARLES WESLEY
SIMEON B. MARSH
1. Je - sus lov - er of my soul, Let me to Thy bo - som fly
While the near - er wa - ters roll, While the tempest sill is high;
2. Oth - er ref - uge have I none, Hangs my help - less soul on Thee;
Leave, oh, leave me not a - lone, Still sup - port and com - fort me.
3. Thou, O Christ, art all I want, More than all in Thee I find;
Raise the fall - en, cheer the faint, Heal the sick and lead the blind.
Hide me, O my Sav - ior, hide, Till the storm of life is past;
All my trust on Thee is stayed, All my help from Thee I bring;
Just and ho - ly is Thy name; I am all un - righteous - ness;
Safe in - to the ha - ven guide, Oh, re - ceive my soul at last.
Cov - er my de - fence - less head With the shad - ow of Thy wing.
Vile and full of sin I am, Thou art full of truth and grace.
Nearer, My God, to Thee
SARAH F. ADAMS
LOWELL MASON
Slowly
1. Near - er, my God, to Thee, Near - er to Thee! E'en tho' it be a cross
2. Tho' like the wan - der - er, The sun gone down, Dark - ness be o - ver me,
3. There let the way ap - pear Steps un - to heav'n; All that Thou sendest me
4. Or if on joy - ful wing Cleav - ing the sky, Sun, moon, and stars forgot,
D.S. Near - er, my God, to Thee,
Fine.
D.S.
That rais - eth me, Still all my song shall be, Near - er, my God, to Thee,
My rest a stone, Yet in my dreams I'd be, Near - er, my God, to Thee,
In mer - cy giv'n; An - gels to beck - on me, Near - er, my God, to Thee,
Up - ward I fly, Still all my song shall be, Near - er, my God, to Thee,
Near - er to Thee.

God Be with You Till We Meet Again

JEREMIAH E. RANKIN — WILLIAM G. TOMER

1. God be with you till we meet a-gain, By His coun-sels guide, up-hold you,
2. God be with you till we meet a-gain, 'Neath His wings pro-tect-ing hide you,
3. God be with you till we meet a-gain, When life's per-ils thick con-found you,
4. God be with you till we meet a-gain, Keep love's ban-ner float-ing o'er you,
With His sheep se-cure-ly fold you, God be with you till we meet a-gain.
Dai-ly man-na still pro-vide you, God be with you till we meet a-gain.
Put His arms un-fail-ing 'round you, God be with you till we meet a-gain.
Smite death's threat'ning wave before you, God be with you till we meet a-gain.
Till we meet, till we meet, Till we meet at Je-sus' feet;
Till we meet, till we meet, till we meet, Till we meet
Till we meet, till we meet, God be with you till we meet a-gain.
Till we meet, till we meet, till we meet,
I Think, When I Read That Sweet Story
JEMIMA T. LUKE
ENGLISH AIR
1. I think when I read that sweet sto-ry of old, When
2. I wish that His hands had been placed on my head, That His
3. Yet still to His foot-stool in pray'r I may go, And

Je - sus was here a - mong men, How He called lit - tle chil - dren like
arms had been thrown a - round me, That I might have seen His kind
ask for a share in His love; And if I thus ear - nest - ly
lambs to His fold, I should like to have been with Him then.
look when He said, "Let the lit - tle ones come un - to Me."
seek Him be - low, I shall see Him and hear Him a - bove.
Jesus Loves Me
ANNA B. WARNER
WILLIAM B. BRADBURY
1. Je - sus loves me! this I know, For the Bi - ble tells me so;
2. Je - sus loves me! He who died Heav - en's gates to o - pen wide;
3. Je - sus loves me! He will stay Close be - side me all the way;
Lit - tle ones to Him be - long; They are weak, but He is strong.
He will wash a - way my sin, Let His lit - tle child come in.
If I love Him, when I die, He will take me home on high.
REFRAIN
Yes, Je - sus loves me! Yes, Je - sus loves me! Yes, Je - sus loves me! The Bi - ble tells me so.

Lead, Kindly Light

On June 16, 1833, John Henry Newman, was on a ship becalmed in the Straits of Bonifacio where he was traveling because of impaired health. At the same time he was being torn by the current spiritual unrest. It was under these conditions that he wrote this noble hymn which invoked aid in solving his great problem and which has since voiced the heartfelt prayers of thousands, for spiritual guidance.

The music was composed by John B. Dykes as he walked through the Strand, one of the busiest thoroughfares of London; a circumstance in striking contrast to that under which the words were written.

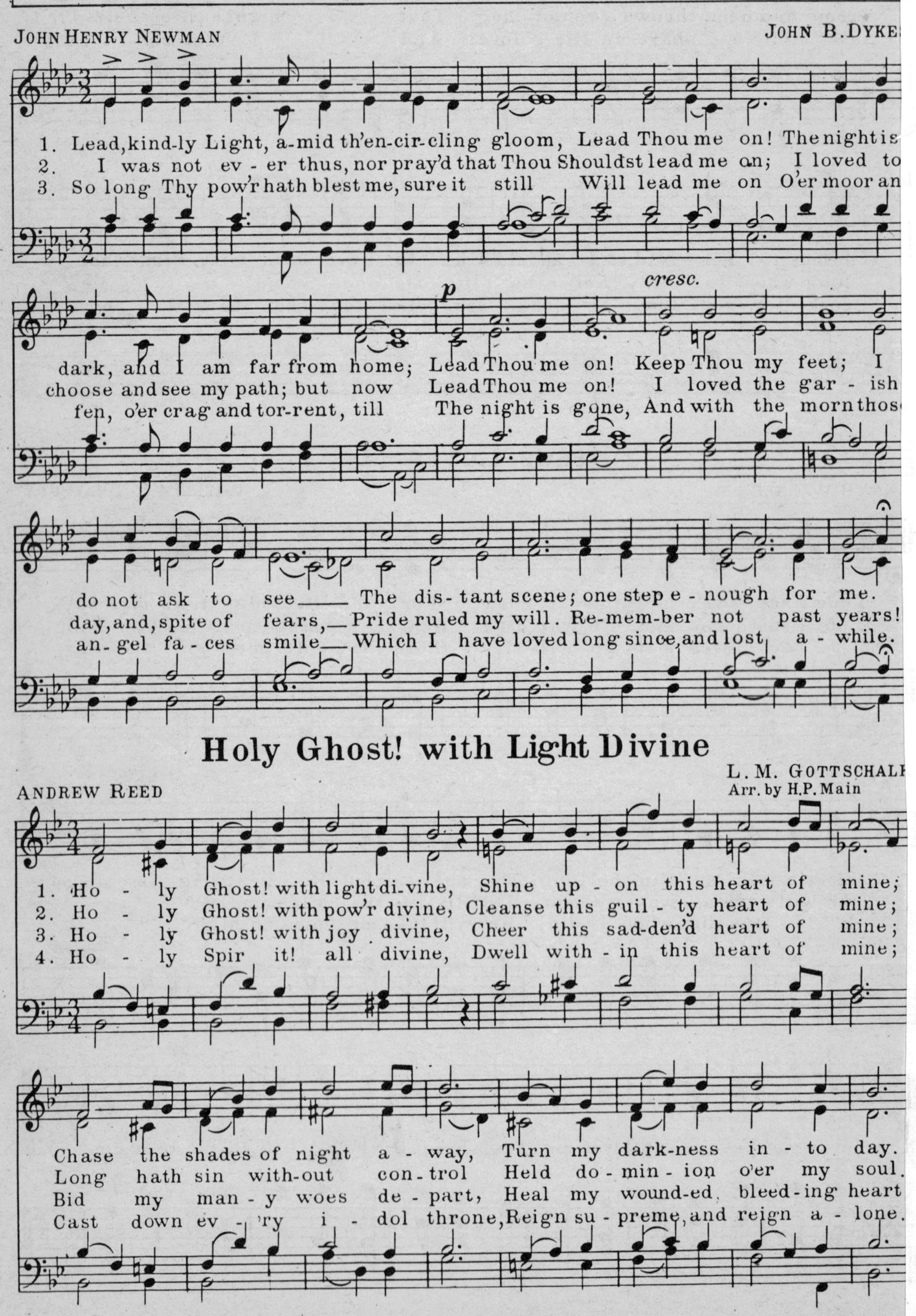
JOHN HENRY NEWMAN
JOHN B. DYKES
1. Lead, kind-ly Light, a-mid th'en-cir-cling gloom, Lead Thou me on! The night is dark, and I am far from home; Lead Thou me on! Keep Thou my feet; I do not ask to see The dis-tant scene; one step e-nough for me.
2. I was not ev-er thus, nor pray'd that Thou Shouldst lead me on; I loved to choose and see my path; but now Lead Thou me on! I loved the gar-ish day, and, spite of fears, Pride ruled my will. Re-mem-ber not past years!
3. So long Thy pow'r hath blest me, sure it still Will lead me on O'er moor and fen, o'er crag and tor-rent, till The night is gone, And with the morn those an-gel fa-ces smile Which I have loved long since, and lost a-while.
p
cresc.
Holy Ghost! with Light Divine
ANDREW REED
L. M. GOTTSCHALK
Arr. by H.P. Main
1. Ho-ly Ghost! with light di-vine, Shine up-on this heart of mine; Chase the shades of night a-way, Turn my dark-ness in-to day.
2. Ho-ly Ghost! with pow'r di-vine, Cleanse this guil-ty heart of mine; Long hath sin with-out con-trol Held do-min-ion o'er my soul.
3. Ho-ly Ghost! with joy divine, Cheer this sad-den'd heart of mine; Bid my man-y woes de-part, Heal my wound-ed, bleed-ing heart.
4. Ho-ly Spir-it! all divine, Dwell with-in this heart of mine; Cast down ev-'ry i-dol throne, Reign su-preme, and reign a-lone.

65
Now Thank We All Our God
ARTIN RINKART
JOHANN CRÜGER
1. Now thank we all our God, With heart and hands and voi - ces,
2. O may this bounteous God, Through all our life be near us,
3. All praise and thanks to God, The Fa - ther, now be giv - en,
Who won-drous things hath done, In whom His earth re - joi - ces:
With ev - er joy - ful hearts, And bless-ed peace to cheer us,
The Son and Him who reigns, With them in high-est Heav - en;
Who from our moth - ers' arms Hath blessed us on our way
And keep us in His grace And guide us when per - plexed,
The one e - ter - nal God, Whom earth and Heav'n a - dore;
With count - less gifts of love, And still is ours to - day.
And free us from all ills, In this world and the next.
For thus it was, is now, And shall be ev - er - more!
Praise God, from Whom All Blessings Flow
(Old Hundredth—The Doxology)
HOMAS KEN
LOUIS BOURGEOIS
Praise God, from whom all blessings flow; Praise Him, all creatures here be-low;
Praise Him a-bove, ye heav'n-ly host; Praise Fa-ther, Son, and Ho - ly Ghost.

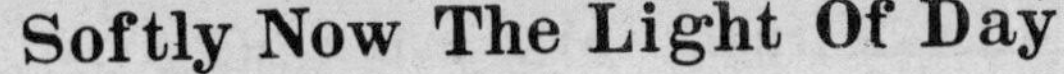
Softly Now The Light Of Day

GEORGE W. DOANE

CARL M. VON WEBER

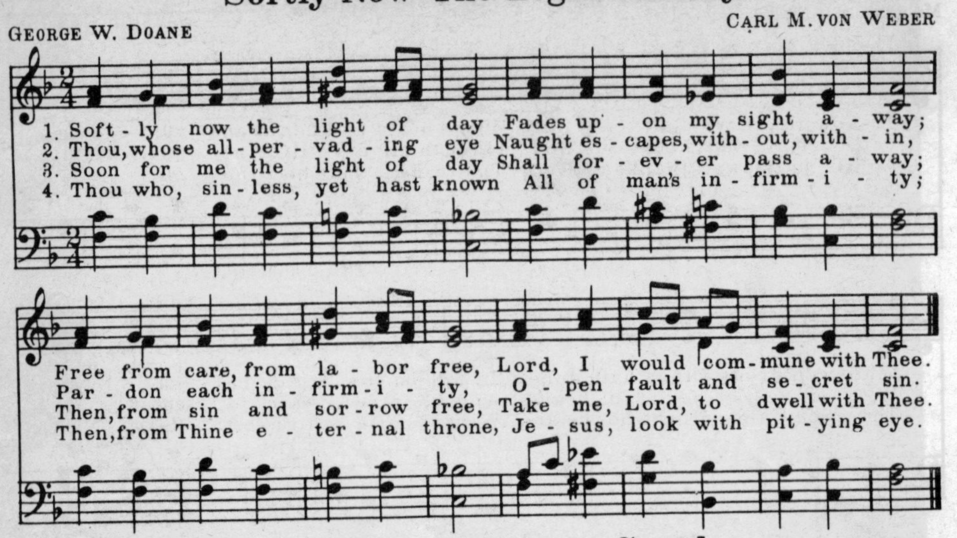
1. Soft - ly now the light of day Fades up - on my sight a - way;
2. Thou, whose all - per - vad - ing eye Naught es - capes, with - out, with - in,
3. Soon for me the light of day Shall for - ev - er pass a - way;
4. Thou who, sin - less, yet hast known All of man's in - firm - i - ty;
Free from care, from la - bor free, Lord, I would com - mune with Thee.
Par - don each in - firm - i - ty, O - pen fault and se - cret sin.
Then, from sin and sor - row free, Take me, Lord, to dwell with Thee.
Then, from Thine e - ter - nal throne, Je - sus, look with pit - ying eye.

The First Christmas Carol

Fear not: for, behold, I bring you good tidings of great joy, which shall be to all people. For unto you is born this day in the city of David a Saviour, which is Christ the Lord. And this shall be a sign unto you; ye shall find the babe wrapped in swaddling clothes lying in a manger. CHORUS: Glory to God in the highest, and on earth peace, good will toward men. — St. Luke's Gospel.

Deck The Halls

OLD WELSH AIR

1. { Deck the halls with boughs of hol - ly, Fa la la la la, la la la la.
'Tis the sea - son to be jol - ly, Fa la la la la, la la la la. }
2. { See the blaz - ing Yule be - fore us, Fa la la la la, la la la la.
Strike the harp and join the cho - rus, Fa la la la la, la la la la. }
3. { Fast a - way the old year pass - es, Fa la la la la, la la la la.
Hail the new, ye lads and lass - es, Fa la la la la, la la la la. }

Don we now our gay ap - par - rel, Fa la la la la la la,
Fol - low me in mer - ry measure, Fa la la la la la la,
Sing we joy - ous all to - geth - er, Fa la la la la la la,

Troll the an - cient Yule - tide car - ol, Fa la la la la, la la la la.
While I tell of Yule - tide treas - ure, Fa la la la la, la la la la.
Heed - less of the wind and weath - er, Fa la la la la, la la la la.

The First Noel

The term Noel is a French word meaning Christmas and is derived from the Latin "natalis" meaning birthday. The songs sung during the Christmas season were known as "Noels," "Nowels" or "Nowells," these names being equivalent to "Carols" in English.

TRADITIONAL
TRADITIONAL
mf
1. The first No - el the an-gel did say Was to certain poor shepherds in fields as they lay:
2. They look-ed_up and_saw_a star Shining in_the East_ beyond them far,
3. This star drew nigh to the north-west, O'er_Beth - le-hem_ it took_its rest,
4. Then en-ter'd in there Wise-men three, Full_rev -'rent - ly_ up - on their knee,
mf
In fields where they lay keeping their sheep On a cold winter's night that was so deep.
And_to_the earth it gave great light, And so it con - tinued both day and night.
And there it_did both stop and stay Right o-ver the place where Je - sus lay.
And of - fer'd there in His_ pres-ence, Their gold and myrrh and frank-incense.
CHORUS
ff
No - el, No - el, No - el, No - el,_Born is the King of Is - ra - el.
ff
Silent Night
JOSEPH MÖHR
FRANZ GRUBER
pp
1. Si - lent night! Ho-ly night! All is calm, all is bright. Round yon virgin mother and Child!
2. Si - lent night! Ho-ly night! Shepherds quake at the sight! Glories stream from Heaven a-far,
3. Si - lent night! Ho-ly night! Son of God, love's pure light Radiant beams from Thy holy face,
Ho - ly Infant, so tender and mild, Sleep in heavenly peace, Sleep in heaven - ly peace.
Heav'nly hosts sing Al-le-lu-ia, Christ, the Savior, is born! Christ, the Savior, is born!
With the dawn of redeeming grace, Je-sus, Lord, at Thy birth, Je - sus, Lord at Thy birth.

It Came upon the Midnight Clear
EDWIN H. SEARS
RICHARD S. WILLIS
1. It came up - on the mid-night clear, That glo-rious song of old,
2. Still thro' the clo - ven skies they come, With peace-ful wings un - furled;
3. For lo! the days are has- t'ning on, By proph-ets seen of old,
From an-gels bend-ing near the earth, To touch their harps of gold:
And still their heav'n-ly mu-sic floats O'er all the wea - ry world:
When with the ev - er - cir-cling years Shall come the time fore - told,
"Peace on the earth, good-will to men From heav'n's all-gra-cious King;"
A - bove its sad and low - ly plains They bend on hov-'ring wing,
When the new heav'n and earth shall own The Prince of Peace their King,
The world in sol - emn still-ness lay To hear the an - gels sing.
And ev - er o'er its Ba - bel sounds The bless - ed an - gels sing.
And the whole world send back the song Which now the an - gels sing.
Hark! the Herald Angels Sing
CHARLES WESLEY
FELIX MENDELSSOHN
1. Hark! the her-ald an-gels sing, "Glo-ry to the new-born King! Peace on earth, and
2. Christ, by high-est heav'n a-dored; Christ, the ev-er-last-ing Lord; Late in time be-
3. Hail! the heav'n-born Prince of Peace! Hail! the Son of Right-eousness! Light and life to

Hark! the Herald Angels Sing—Concluded
mer-cy mild, God and sin-ners re-con-ciled". Joy-ful, all ye na-tions, rise,
hold Him come, Off-spring of the fa-vored one. Veiled in flesh, the God-head see;
all He brings, Ris'n with heal-ing in His wings. Mild He lays His glo-ry by,
Join the tri-umph of the skies; With th'an-gel-ic host proclaim, "Christ is born in
Hail th'in-car-nate De-i-ty Pleased, as man with men to dwell, Je-sus, our Im-
Born that man no more may die: Born to raise the sons of earth, Born to give them
Beth-le-hem."
man-u-el!
sec-ond birth.
Hark! the herald an-gels sing, "Glo-ry to the new-born King!"
Glad Christmas Bells
1. Glad Christmas bells, your mu-sic tells The sweet and pleasant sto-ry;
2. No pal-ace hall its ceil-ing tall His king-ly head spread o-ver,
3. Nor rai-ment gay, as there He lay, A-dorn'd the in-fant stranger;
4. But from a-far, a splendid star The wise men westward turning;
How came to earth, in low-ly birth, The Lord of life and glo-ry.
There on-ly stood a sta-ble rude The heav-enly Babe to cov-er.
Poor, hum-ble Child of moth-er mild, She laid Him in a man-ger.
The live-long night saw pure and bright, A-bove His birth place burn-ing.

From Every Spire on Christmas Eve

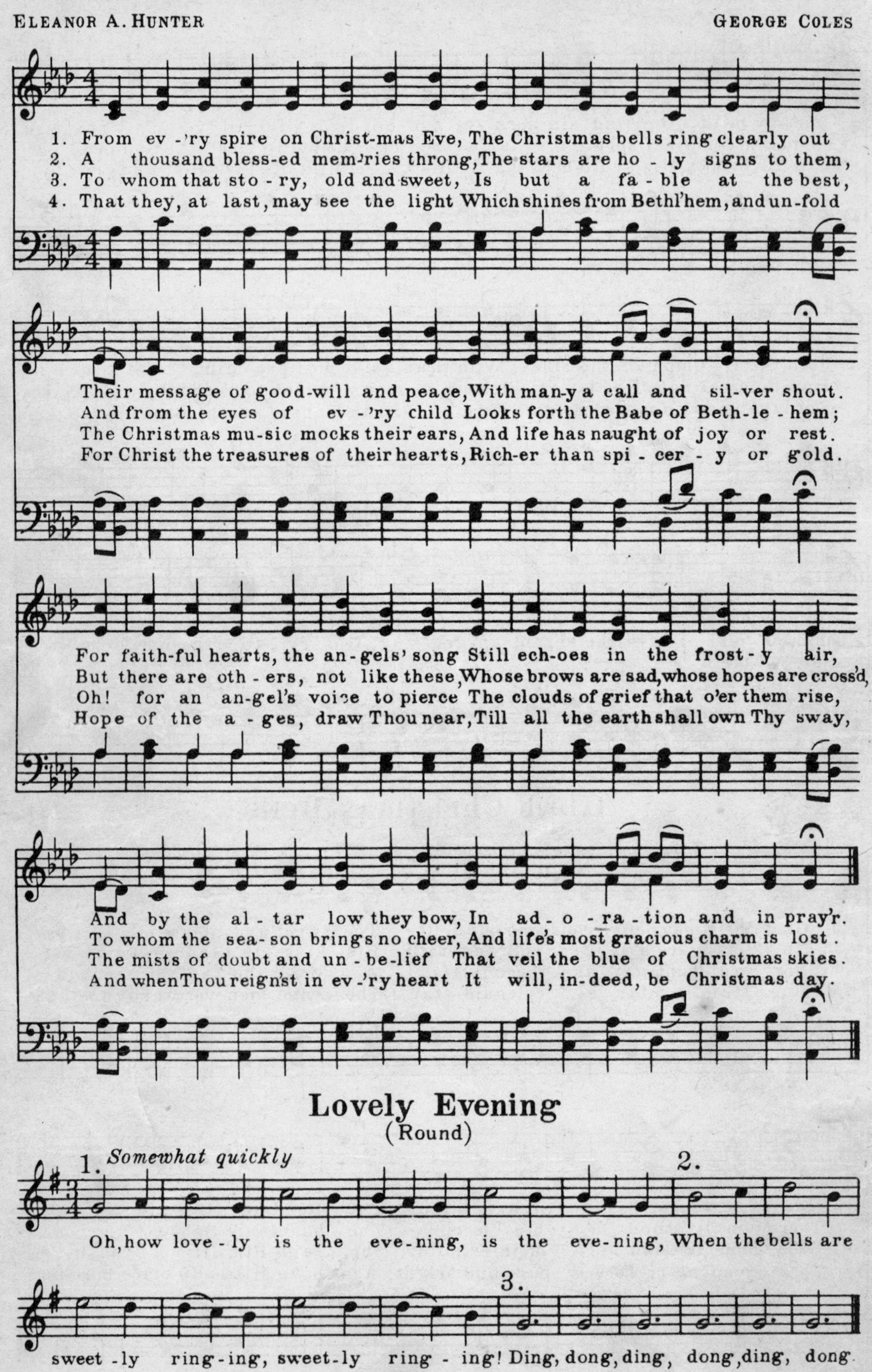
ELEANOR A. HUNTER
GEORGE COLES
1. From ev-'ry spire on Christ-mas Eve, The Christmas bells ring clearly out
2. A thousand bless-ed mem-'ries throng, The stars are ho-ly signs to them,
3. To whom that sto-ry, old and sweet, Is but a fa-ble at the best,
4. That they, at last, may see the light Which shines from Bethl'hem, and un-fold
Their message of good-will and peace, With man-y a call and sil-ver shout.
And from the eyes of ev-'ry child Looks forth the Babe of Beth-le-hem;
The Christmas mu-sic mocks their ears, And life has naught of joy or rest.
For Christ the treasures of their hearts, Rich-er than spi-cer-y or gold.
For faith-ful hearts, the an-gels' song Still ech-oes in the frost-y air,
But there are oth-ers, not like these, Whose brows are sad, whose hopes are cross'd,
Oh! for an an-gel's voice to pierce The clouds of grief that o'er them rise,
Hope of the a-ges, draw Thou near, Till all the earth shall own Thy sway,
And by the al-tar low they bow, In ad-o-ra-tion and in pray'r.
To whom the sea-son brings no cheer, And life's most gracious charm is lost.
The mists of doubt and un-be-lief That veil the blue of Christmas skies.
And when Thou reign'st in ev-'ry heart It will, in-deed, be Christmas day.
Lovely Evening
(Round)
1. Somewhat quickly
2.
Oh, how love-ly is the eve-ning, is the eve-ning, When the bells are
3.
sweet-ly ring-ing, sweet-ly ring-ing! Ding, dong, ding, dong, ding, dong

Joy to the World!
ISAAC WATTS
GEORGE F. HANDEL
Arr. by Lowell Mason
1. Joy to the world! The Lord is come; Let earth re-ceive her King; — Let
2. Joy to the world! The Sav - ior reigns; Let men their songs em-ploy; — While
3. No more let sin and sor - row grow, Nor thorns in - fest the ground; — He
4. He rules the world with truth and grace, And makes the na-tions prove — The
ev - 'ry heart pre-pare Him room, And heav'n and nature sing, And
fields and floods, rocks, hills and plains, Re-peat the sounding joy, Re -
comes to make His bless-ings flow Far as the curse is found, Far
glo - ries of His righteous - ness, And wonders of His love, And
And heav'n, and heav'n and nature
heav'n and na-ture sing, And heav'n, and heav'n and na - ture sing.
peat the sounding joy, Re - peat, re - peat the sounding joy.
as the curse is found, Far as, far as the curse is found.
won-ders of His love, And wonders, and won - ders of His love.
sing, And heav'n and nature sing,
I Heard the Bells on Christmas Day
HENRY W. LONGFELLOW
J. BAPTISTE CALKIN
1. I heard the bells on Christmas day Their old fa-mil-iar car - ols play,
2. I thought how, as the day had come, The bel-fries of all Chris-ten-dom
3. And in despair I bow'd my head: "There is no peace on earth," I said,
4. Then pealed the bells more loud and deep: "God is not dead, nor doth He sleep;
5. Till, ring - ing, sing-ing on its way, The world revolved from night to day,
And wild and sweet the words repeat Of peace on earth, good will to men.
Had roll'd a-long th'un-bro-ken song Of peace on earth, good will to men.
"For hate is strong, and mocks the song Of peace on earth, good will to men."
The wrong shall fail, the right pre-vail, With peace on earth, good will to men."
A voice, a chime, a chant sub-lime, Of peace on earth, good will to men!

O Come, All Ye Faithful

(Adeste Fideles)

This hymn is supposed to have been written during the 13th century. It is one of the most popular of the old Latin Hymns and is used in all Christian Churches especially at Christmas. The author of the words is unknown. It was translated by F. Oakley, in 1841. The music is supposed to have been written by John Reading, an English organist of the 18th century.

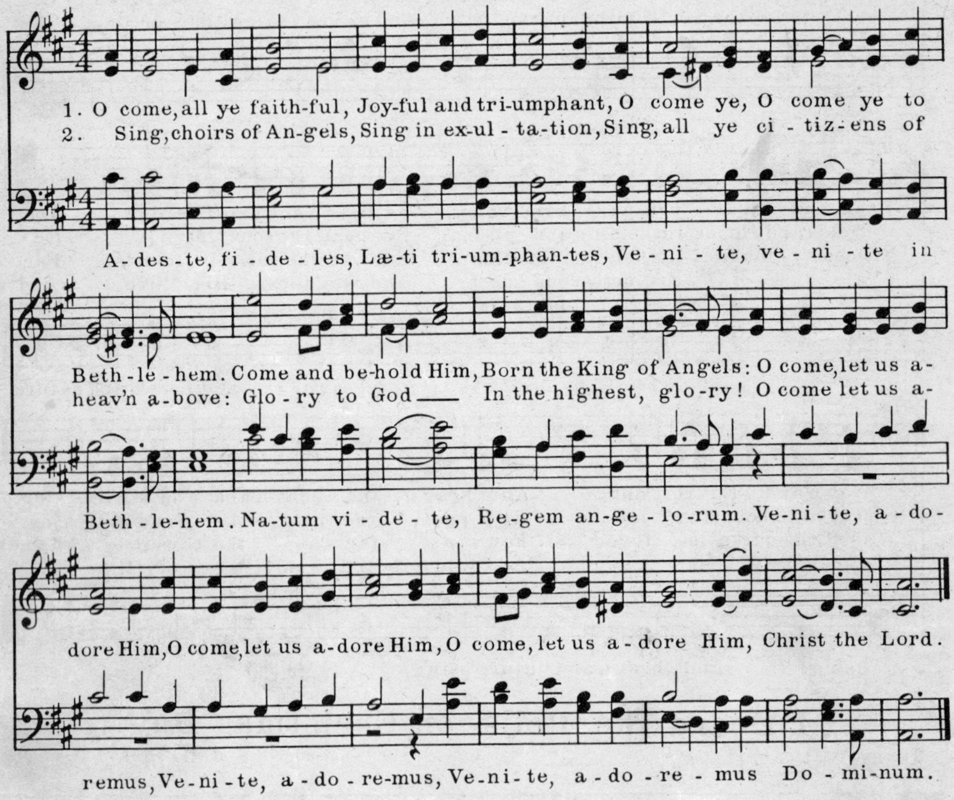

1. O come, all ye faith-ful, Joy-ful and tri-umphant, O come ye, O come ye to
2. Sing, choirs of An-gels, Sing in ex-ul - ta-tion, Sing, all ye ci - tiz-ens of

A-des-te, fi - de - les, Læ-ti tri-um-phan-tes, Ve - ni - te, ve - ni - te in

Beth-le-hem. Come and be-hold Him, Born the King of Angels: O come, let us a-
heav'n a-bove: Glo-ry to God ___ In the highest, glo-ry! O come let us a-

Beth-le-hem. Na-tum vi - de - te, Re-gem an-ge - lo-rum. Ve-ni-te, a-do-

dore Him, O come, let us a-dore Him, O come, let us a-dore Him, Christ the Lord.

remus, Ve-ni-te, a-do-re-mus, Ve-ni-te, a-do-re-mus Do-mi-num.

How Firm a Foundation

1. How firm a foundation, ye saints of the Lord,
Is laid for your faith in His excellent Word!
What more can He say than to you
He hath said,
To you, who for refuge to Jesus have fled?
To you, who for refuge to Jesus have fled?

Fear not, I am with thee, O be not dismayed,
For I am thy God and will still give thee aid;
I'll strengthen thee, help thee, and
cause thee to stand,
Upheld by My righteous, omnipotent hand,
Upheld by My righteous, omnipotent hand.

Luther's Cradle Hymn

(Away in a Manger)

MARTIN LUTHER

J. B. HERBERT

Arr. by J.W.B.

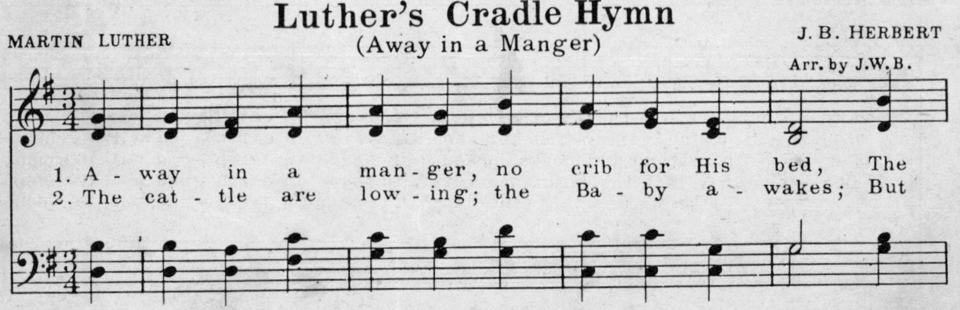
1. A - way in a man-ger, no crib for His bed, The
2. The cat - tle are low - ing; the Ba - by a - wakes; But

Luther's Cradle Hymn—Continued
lit-tle Lord Je-sus lay down His sweet head. The stars in the heav-ens Looked
lit-tle Lord Je-sus no cry-ing He makes. I love Thee, Lord Je-sus Look
down where He lay, The lit-tle Lord Je-sus a-sleep on the hay.
down from the sky, And stay by my cra-dle till morn-ing is nigh.
17
O, Little Town of Bethlehem
PHILLIPS BROOKS
LEWIS H. REDNER
1. O lit-tle town of Beth-le-hem, How still we see thee lie;
2. For Christ is born of Ma-ry; And gath-ered all a-bove,
3. How si-lent-ly, how si-lent-ly, The Won-drous Gift is giv'n!
4. O ho-ly Child of Beth-le-hem, De-scend to us, we pray;
A-bove thy deep and dream-less sleep The si-lent stars go by:
While mor-tals sleep, the an-gels keep Their watch of wond'ring love.
So God im-parts to hu-man hearts The bless-ings of His heav'n.
Cast out our sin, and en-ter in, Be born in us to-day.
Yet in thy dark streets shin-eth The ev-er-last-ing Light;
O morn-ing stars, to-geth-er Pro-claim the ho-ly birth;
No ear may hear His com-ing, But in this world of sin,
We hear the Christ-mas an-gels The great glad tid-ings tell;
The hopes and fears of all the years Are met in thee to-night.
And prais-es sing to God the King, And peace to men on earth.
Where meek souls will re-ceive Him, still The dear Christ en-ters in.
O come to us, a-bide with us, Our Lord E-man-u-el.

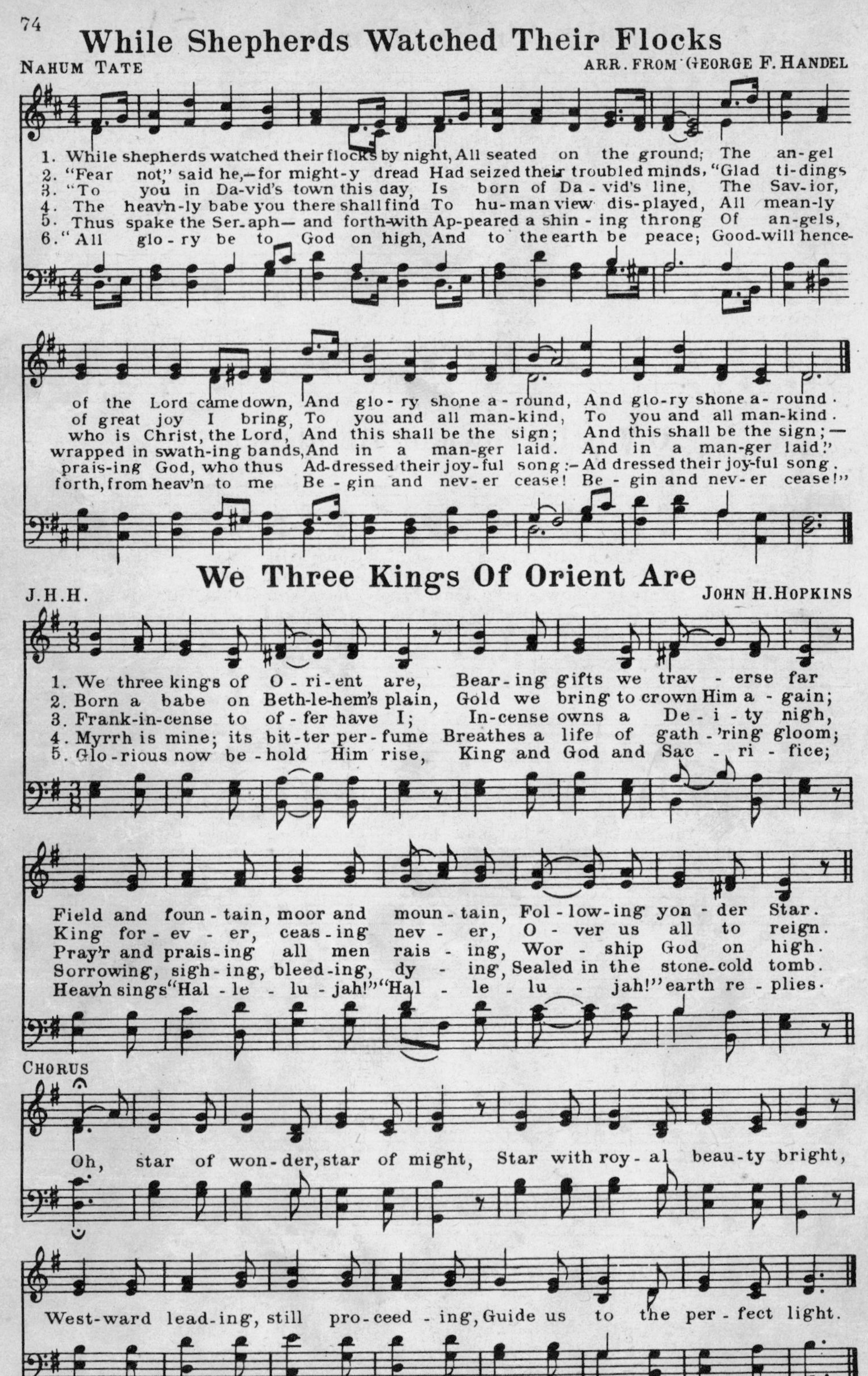
While Shepherds Watched Their Flocks
Nahum Tate
Arr. from George F. Handel
1. While shepherds watched their flocks by night, All seated on the ground; The an-gel
2. "Fear not," said he,—for might-y dread Had seized their troubled minds, "Glad ti-dings
3. "To you in Da-vid's town this day, Is born of Da-vid's line, The Sav-ior,
4. The heav'n-ly babe you there shall find To hu-man view dis-played, All mean-ly
5. Thus spake the Ser-aph— and forth-with Ap-peared a shin - ing throng Of an-gels,
6. "All glo-ry be to God on high, And to the earth be peace; Good-will hence-
of the Lord came down, And glo-ry shone a-round, And glo-ry shone a-round.
of great joy I bring, To you and all man-kind, To you and all man-kind.
who is Christ, the Lord, And this shall be the sign; And this shall be the sign;—
wrapped in swath-ing bands, And in a man-ger laid. And in a man-ger laid."
prais-ing God, who thus Ad-dressed their joy-ful song:—Ad dressed their joy-ful song.
forth, from heav'n to me Be - gin and nev - er cease! Be - gin and nev - er cease!"
We Three Kings Of Orient Are
J.H.H.
John H. Hopkins
1. We three kings of O - ri - ent are, Bear-ing gifts we trav - erse far
2. Born a babe on Beth-le-hem's plain, Gold we bring to crown Him a - gain;
3. Frank-in-cense to of - fer have I; In-cense owns a De - i - ty nigh,
4. Myrrh is mine; its bit-ter per-fume Breathes a life of gath - 'ring gloom;
5. Glo-rious now be-hold Him rise, King and God and Sac - ri - fice;
Field and foun - tain, moor and moun - tain, Fol - low-ing yon - der Star.
King for - ev - er, ceas-ing nev - er, O - ver us all to reign.
Pray'r and prais-ing all men rais - ing, Wor - ship God on high.
Sorrowing, sigh-ing, bleed-ing, dy - ing, Sealed in the stone-cold tomb.
Heav'n sings "Hal - le - lu - jah!" "Hal - le - lu - jah!" earth re - plies.
Chorus
Oh, star of won-der, star of might, Star with roy - al beau-ty bright,
West-ward lead-ing, still pro-ceed - ing, Guide us to the per - fect light.

Jolly Old Saint Nicholas
TRADITIONAL
TRADITIONAL
1. Jol-ly old Saint Ni-cho-las, Lean your ear this way! Don't you tell a sin-gle soul What I'm going to say; Christmas Eve is com-ing soon; Now, you dear old man, Whisper what you'll bring to me; Tell me if you can.
2. When the clock is striking twelve, When I'm fast a-sleep, Down the chimney broad and black, With your pack you'll creep; All the stock-ings you will find Hang-ing in a row; Mine will be the short-est one, You'll be sure to know.
3. John-ny wants a pair of skates; Su-sy wants a dol-ly; Nel-lie wants a sto-ry book; She thinks dolls are fol-ly; As for me, my lit-tle brain Is-n't ver-y bright; Choose for me, old San-ta Claus, What you think is right.
Up On The House-Top
TRADITIONAL
TRADITIONAL
1. Up on the house-top rein-deer pause, Out jumps good old San-ta Claus; Down thro' the chimney with lots of toys, All for the lit-tle ones, Christmas joys.
2. First comes the stocking of lit-tle Nell; Oh, dear San-ta, fill it well; Give her a dol-lie that laughs and crys-One that will open and shut her eyes.
3. Next comes the stocking of lit-tle Will; Oh, just see what a glorious fill! Here is a ham-mer and lots of tacks, Al-so a ball and a whip that cracks.
CHORUS
Ho, ho, ho! who would-n't go! Ho, ho, ho! who would-n't go!
Up on the house-top, click, click, click, Down thro' the chimney with good Saint Nick.

The six following Nursery Rhymes, which all children know and love, date back so many years that their origin is more or less obscure. The verses in the form used here probably came from England and most of the settings are by J.W. Elliott.

Baa! Baa! Black Sheep

Hey, Diddle, Diddle

Dickory, Dickory, Dock

Lively
Baa! Baa! Black sheep, have you an-y wool? Yes, sir,
yes, sir! Three bags full, One for my mas-ter, and one for my
dame, But none for the naughty boy that cries in the lane.
Lively
Hey, diddle, diddle, The cat and the fiddle, The cow jump'd o-ver the moon, The
lit-tle dog laughed To see such sport, And the dish ran af-ter the spoon.
Lively
Dick-o-ry, dick-o-ry, dock; The mouse ran up the clock; The
clock struck "one," The mouse ran down; Dick-o-ry, dick-o-ry, dock.

Little Jack Horner

Lively
Lit-tle Jack Horner sat in a cor-ner, Eat-ing a Christmas pie, He
put in his thumb, And pulled out a plum, And said "What a good boy am I."
Little Bo-Peep
Moderately
mf
Lit-tle Bo-Peep has lost her sheep, And can't tell where to find them,
Leave them a-lone, and they'll come home, Wagging their tails be-hind them.
See-Saw, Margery Daw
Lively
mf
See-saw, Mar-ge-ry Daw, Jack shall have a new mas-ter,
He shall have but a pen-ny a day, Be-cause he won't work any fast-er.

Indian Lullaby

HENRY W. LONGFELLOW — WALTER H. AIKEN

p
Dreamily
p
1. Rock - a - bye, my lit - tle ow - let, In thy mos - sy, sway - ing nest,
2. Hush - a - bye, my lit - tle ow - let, Ma - ny voic - es sing to thee,
3. Sleep, O sleep, my lit - tle ow - let, Thro' our tent the moon shines bright,
With thy lit - tle wood - land broth - ers, Close thine eyes and take thy rest.
"Hush - a - bye," the wa - ter whis - pers, "Hush!" re - plies the tall pine tree.
Like a great eye it will watch thee, Sleep till comes the morning light.
To whoo, to whoo, to whoo, to

Indian Lullaby—Continued
whoo.
Used by special permission of The Willis Music Company, Cincinnati, Ohio, owners of the copyright.
The Robin And Chicken
(Scale Song)
WALTER H. AIKEN
1. A plump lit - tle rob - in flew down from a tree, To
2. Said the chick "What a queer look - ing chick - en is that, Its
3. "Can you sing," rob - in asked, and the chick - en said, "No," But
hunt for a worm which it happened to see, A frisk-y young chicken came
wings are so long and its bo - dy so flat!" While rob - in remarked loud e -
asked in its turn if the rob - in could crow, So the bird sought a tree, and the
scamper - ing by, And gazed at the rob - in with won-der - ing eye.
nough to be heard, "Dear me, an ex - ceed - ing - ly strange looking bird!"
chicken a wall; And each tho't the oth - er knew nothing at all.

Robin Redbreast

ALLINGHAM
FRIEDRICH KÜCKEN
1. Good - bye, good-bye to Sum-mer, For the Sum-mer's nearly done,
2. Bright yel - low, red and or - ange, The leaves come down in hosts,
3. The fire-side for the crick - et, The wheat-stack for the mouse,
For the Summer's near-ly done; The gar-den smil-ing faint - ly, Cool
The leaves come down in hosts, The trees are In - dian prin - ces, But
The wheat-stack for the mouse, When trembling night-winds whistle And
breez-es in the sun; The thrushes now are si-lent, Our swallows flown a-
soon they'll turn to ghosts; The leath'ry pears and apples Hang russet on the
moan all round the house; The frost-y ways, like i-ron, The branches, plum'd with
way, But Rob-in's here in coat of brown, And scar-let breast-knot gay.
bough; 'Tis Au-tumn, Au-tumn, Au-tumn, late, 'Twill soon be Win-ter now.
snow, A - las! in Win-ter dead and dark, Where can poor Rob-in go?
CHORUS
O Rob-in, Rob-in Red-breast, O Rob-in, Rob-in dear, O
Rob-in sings so sweet - ly in the fall-ing of the year.

Cradle Song

KARL SIMROCK
Translated by Arthur Westbrook

JOHANNES BRAHMS

1. Lul-la - by and good night! With
2. Lul-la - by and good night! Those
ro - ses be - dight, — Creep in - to thy bed, There pil - low thy
blue eyes close tight, — Bright an-gels are near, So sleep with-out
head If God will thou shalt wake, When the morn - ing doth
fear. They will guard thee from harm, With fair dream-land's sweet
break, If God will thou shalt wake, When the morn-ing doth break.
charm, They will guard thee from harm, With fair dream-land's sweet charm.

Singing In The Rain

ELIZABETH AKERS ALLEN
FRANZ JOSEPH HAYDN
1.Where the elm-tree branches By the rain are stirr'd, Careless of the show-er
2.From their heavy frin-ges, Pour their drops a-main; Still the bird is sing-ing,
3.Cheerful summer prophet! List'ning to thy song, How my faint-ing spir-it
Swings a lit-tle bird: Clouds may frown and darken, Drops may fall in vain,
Sing - ing in the rain. O thou hope-ful sing-er, Whom my faith perceives
Grow-eth glad and strong. Let the black clouds gather, Let the sunshine wane,
Lit-tle heeds the warbler Sing-ing in the rain. Dimmer fall the shad-ows,
To a dove transfigured, Bring-ing ol-ive leaves; Ol - ive leaves of prom-ise,
If I may but join thee, Sing-ing in the rain. Let the black clouds gather,
Mist-ier grows the air, Still the black clouds gather, Dark'ning here and there.
Types of joy to be; How in doubt and tri-al Learns my heart of thee.
Let the sunshine wane, If I may but join thee, Sing-ing in the rain.
Good Morning To You
PATTI S. HILL
MILDRED HILL
Brightly
Good morn - ing to you, Good morn - ing to you,

Good Morning To You – Continued
Good - morn - ing, dear chil - dren, Good - morn - ing to all.
Used by permission. Copyright by Clayton F. Summy Co.
Waiting To Grow
WALTER H. AIKEN
1. Lit - tle white snow-drop, just wak - ing up, Vi - o - let,
2. Think what a host of queer lit - tle seeds, Of flow-ers and
dai - sy and sweet but - ter - cup; Un-der the leaves and the
mos - ses and ferns and weeds Are un-der the leaves and the
ice and the snow, Wait - ing, wait - ing, Wait-ing to grow.
ice and the snow, Wait - ing, wait - ing, Wait-ing to grow.
Used by special permission of The Willis Music Company, Cincinnati, Ohio, owners of the copyright.

Twinkle, Little Star
JANE TAYLOR
Not too slowly
1. Twin-kle, twin-kle, lit - tle star; How I won-der what you are,
2. When the blaz-ing sun is gone, When he noth-ing shines up - on,
3. Then the trav'ller in the dark Thanks you for your ti - ny spark;
4. In the dark blue sky you keep, While you thro' my win - dow peep,
Up a - bove the world so high, Like a dia-mond in the sky!
Then you show your lit - tle light, Twin-kle, twin-kle all the night.
He could not see where to go, If you did not twinkle so.
And you nev - er shut your eye, Till the sun is in the sky.
Twin-kle, twin-kle, lit - tle star, How I won-der what you are.
A Little Man
FOLK SONG
sung in Hansel and Gretel
HUMPERDINCK
Moderately quick
mf
A ti-ny lit-tle man stands in for - est dim, A cunning lit-tle
man-tle he wears on him, Who can this fig-ure be, stand-ing 'neath a
ritard
for-est tree, With the man-tle hang-ing down to his knee?

I Will Sing A Lullaby
17th Century
ENGLISH CRADLE SONG
Somewhat slowly
1. Gold-en slumbers kiss your eyes, Smiles awake you when you rise; Sleep, pretty lov'd ones, do not cry, And I will sing a lul-la-by,
2. Care is heav-y, there-fore sleep, Mother here safe watch will keep; Sleep, pretty lov'd ones, do not cry, And I will sing a lul-la-by,
Lul-la-by, lul-la-by, lul - la - by.
The Cuckoo
GERMAN FOLK SONG
1. Cuck-oo, cuck-oo, wel-come thy song! Win-ter is go-ing, Soft breez-es blow-ing, Spring time, spring time, soon will be here.
2. Cuck-oo, cuck-oo, war-ble a-way; Bring the sweet flow-ers, Sun-shine and show-ers, Spring time, spring time, do not de-lay.
Hop, Hop, Hop!
GERMAN FOLK SONG
1. Hop, hop, hop! Nim-ble as a top, Where 'tis smooth and where 'tis stony, Trudge a-long, my lit-tle po-ny, Hop, hop, hop, hop, hop! Nim-ble as a top.
2. Whoa, whoa, whoa! How like fun you go! Ver-y well, my lit-tle po-ny, Safe's our jaunt tho' rough and stony, Spare, spare, spare, spare, spare! Sure enough we're there.
3. Here, here, here! Yes my po-ny dear; Now with oats and hay I'll treat you, And with smiles will ev-er greet you, Po-ny, po-ny dear! Yes my po-ny dear.

Lightly Row

GERMAN FOLK SONG

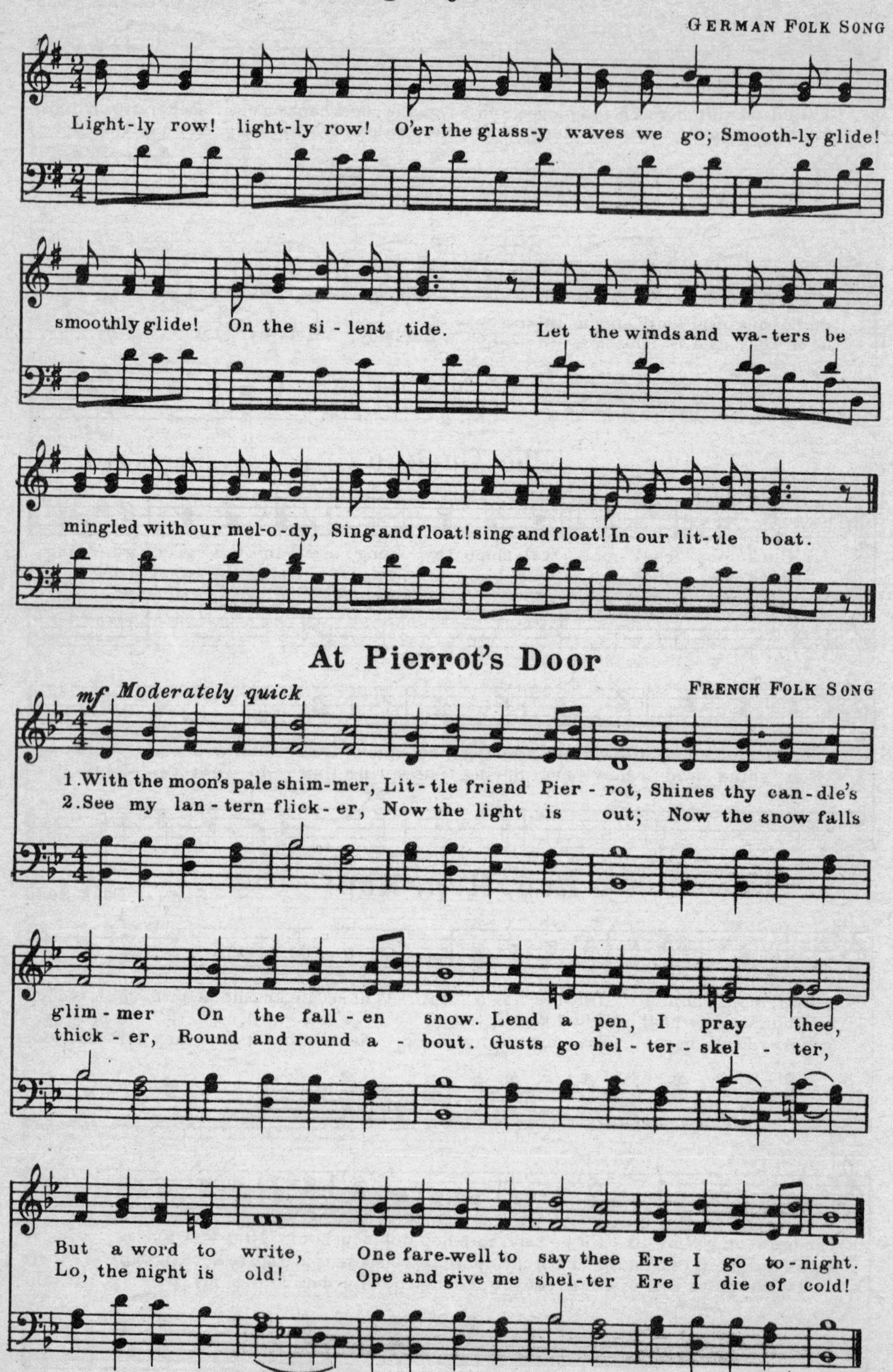
Light-ly row! light-ly row! O'er the glass-y waves we go; Smooth-ly glide!
smoothly glide! On the si-lent tide. Let the winds and wa-ters be
mingled with our mel-o-dy, Sing and float! sing and float! In our lit-tle boat.
At Pierrot's Door
mf Moderately quick
FRENCH FOLK SONG
1. With the moon's pale shim-mer, Lit-tle friend Pier-rot, Shines thy can-dle's
2. See my lan-tern flick-er, Now the light is out; Now the snow falls
glim-mer On the fall-en snow. Lend a pen, I pray thee,
thick-er, Round and round a-bout. Gusts go hel-ter-skel-ter,
But a word to write, One fare-well to say thee Ere I go to-night.
Lo, the night is old! Ope and give me shel-ter Ere I die of cold!

When I Was A Lady

Waltz time ENGLISH SINGING GAME

mf

1.When I was a la - dy, a la - dy, a la - dy, And when I was a la - dy, a la - dy was I, *mf* And this way, and that way, And this way, and that way, And when *cresc.* I was a la - dy, a la - dy was I.

2. When I was a young girl, etc.
3. When I was a dancer, etc.
4. When I was a young man, etc.
5. When I was a soldier, etc.

For this motion song a leader is chosen who, while the first verse is being sung, imitates the actions of a lady, curtseying first to the left then to the right. Another leader is chosen for each of the characters in the other verses. The other children imitate the motions of the leader.

Susy, Little Susy

TRANSLATION

FOLK SONG
sung in Hansel and Gretel
HUMPERDINCK

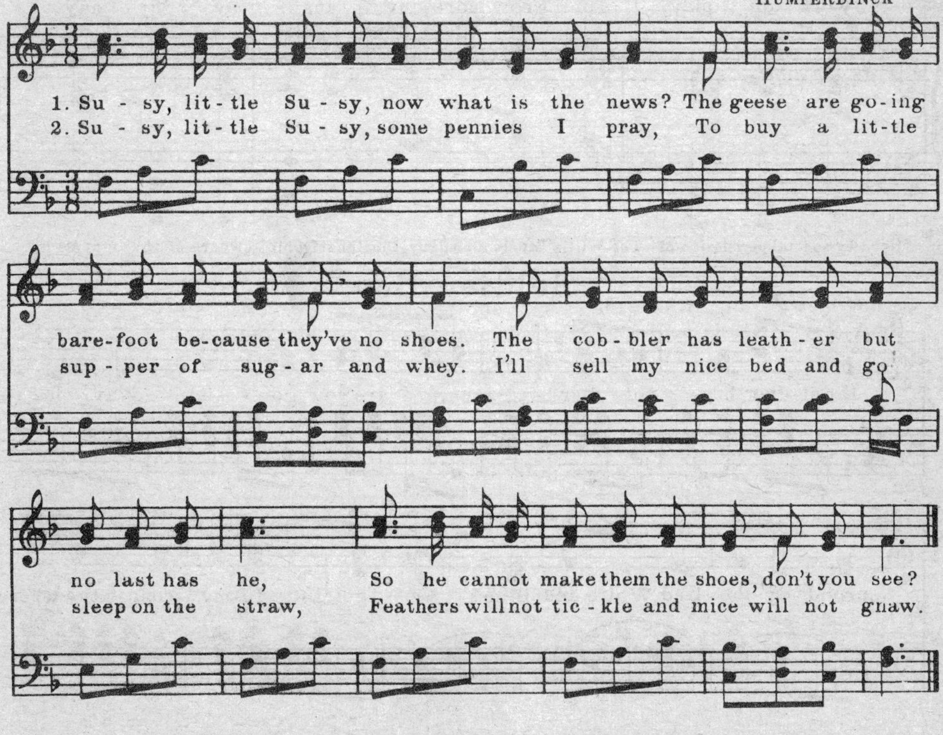

1. Su - sy, lit - tle Su - sy, now what is the news? The geese are go - ing bare - foot be - cause they've no shoes. The cob - bler has leath - er but no last has he, So he cannot make them the shoes, don't you see?

2. Su - sy, lit - tle Su - sy, some pennies I pray, To buy a lit - tle sup - per of sug - ar and whey. I'll sell my nice bed and go sleep on the straw, Feathers will not tic - kle and mice will not gnaw.

Morning Prayer

Reverently

K. D. WIGGINS

1. Fa-ther, we thank Thee for the night,
2. Help us to do the things we should;

And for the pleas-ant morn-ing light; For rest and food and
To be to oth-ers kind and good; In all we do, in

lov-ing care, And all that makes the world so fair.
work or play, To grow more lov-ing ev-'ry day.

Soldier Boy

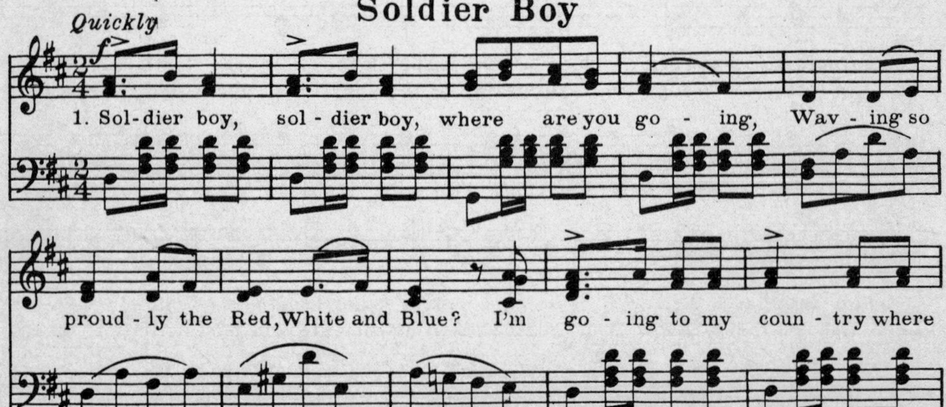
Quickly
f
1. Sol-dier boy, sol-dier boy, where are you go-ing, Wav-ing so
proud-ly the Red, White and Blue? I'm go-ing to my coun-try where

Soldier Boy—Continued

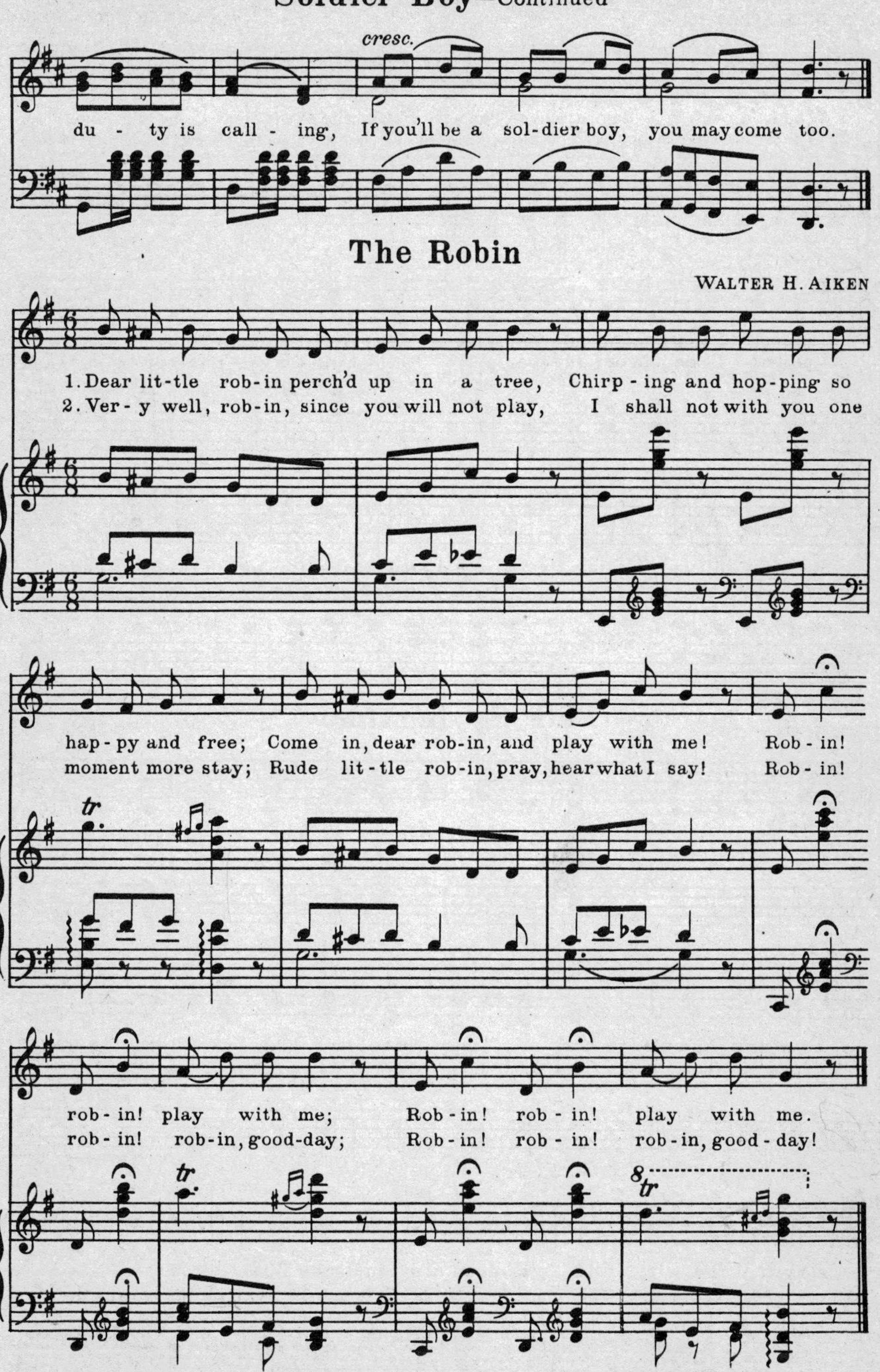
cresc.
du - ty is call - ing, If you'll be a sol-dier boy, you may come too.
The Robin
WALTER H. AIKEN
1. Dear lit-tle rob-in perch'd up in a tree, Chirp - ing and hop-ping so
2. Ver - y well, rob-in, since you will not play, I shall not with you one
hap - py and free; Come in, dear rob-in, and play with me! Rob - in!
moment more stay; Rude lit - tle rob-in, pray, hear what I say! Rob - in!
tr
rob - in! play with me; Rob - in! rob - in! play with me.
rob - in! rob-in, good-day; Rob - in! rob - in! rob - in, good - day!
tr
8
tr

January and February
JANE B. WALTERS
GERMAN FOLK SONG
1. When Jan-u-ar-y days are here, The air is crisp, the sky is clear, Come join our outdoor plays, Come join our out-door plays. For o'er the ice we're glid - ing, Or down the hill we're sliding, Or in a bob-sled rid-ing In Jan-u-ar-y days.
2. When Feb-ru-ary north winds blow, Lake, hill and road are heaped with snow, Come join our in-door plays, Come join our in-door plays. Like lit-tle gob-lins hop-ping The feath-ery corn is popping In salt-y pan soon dropping, In Feb-ru-ar-y days.
'Tis Springtime
JANE B. WALTERS
SÜSSMAYER
1. 'Tis spring time, 'tis spring time, Cold win-ter is past; Warm breez-es are blow-ing And May's here at last; The birds are re - turn-ing, Their songs fill the air; And mea-dows are smil-ing With blossoms so fair.
2. 'Tis spring time, 'tis spring time, All na-ture's re-born; Shy flow-ers, fresh grass-es The hill-sides a - dorn; The or-chards and wood-lands With col - ors are gay, The glad earth re-joic-es Through all the bright day.

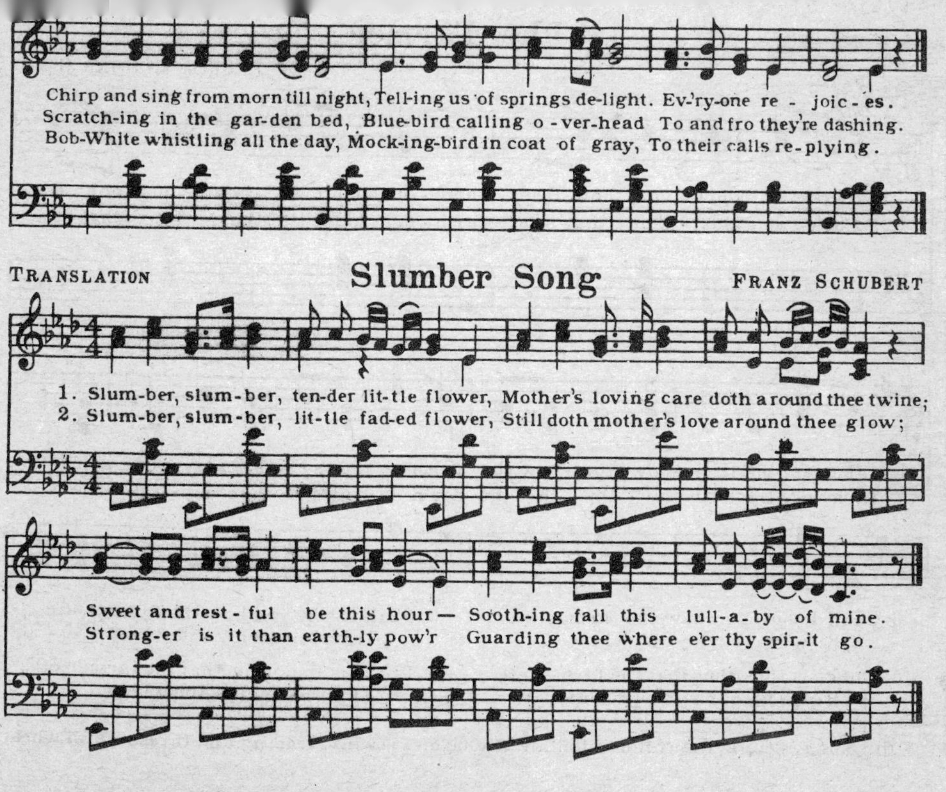
Chirp and sing from morn till night, Tell-ing us of springs de-light. Ev-'ry-one re - joic - es.
Scratch-ing in the gar-den bed, Blue-bird calling o - ver-head To and fro they're dashing.
Bob-White whistling all the day, Mock-ing-bird in coat of gray, To their calls re-plying.
TRANSLATION
Slumber Song
FRANZ SCHUBERT
1. Slum-ber, slum-ber, ten-der lit-tle flower, Mother's loving care doth around thee twine;
2. Slum-ber, slum-ber, lit-tle fad-ed flower, Still doth mother's love around thee glow;
Sweet and rest - ful be this hour— Sooth-ing fall this lull-a-by of mine.
Strong-er is it than earth-ly pow'r Guarding thee where e'er thy spir-it go.

The Farmer

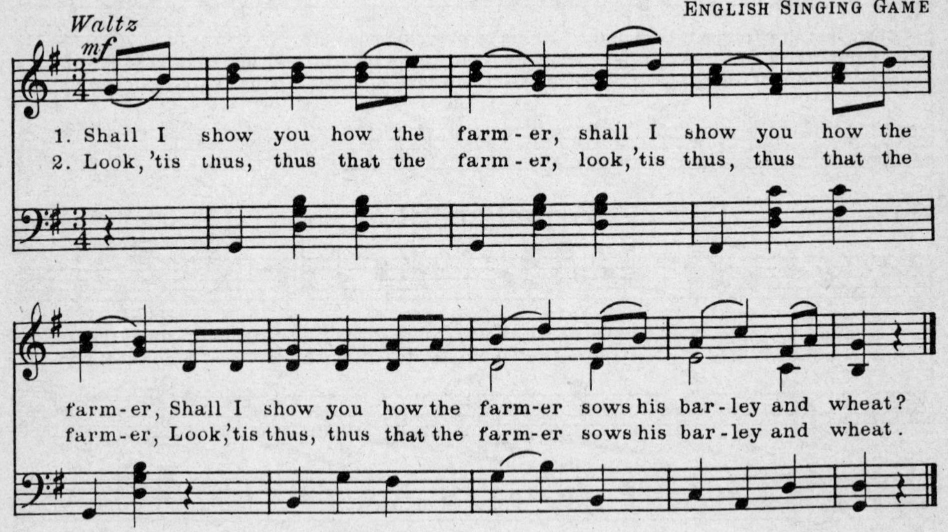
ENGLISH SINGING GAME
Waltz
mf
1. Shall I show you how the farm - er, shall I show you how the farm-er, Shall I show you how the farm-er sows his bar - ley and wheat?
2. Look, 'tis thus, thus that the farm - er, look, 'tis thus, thus that the farm-er, Look, 'tis thus, thus that the farm-er sows his bar - ley and wheat.

3. Shall I show you how the farmer, etc.
Reaps his barley and wheat.

4. Look 'tis thus, thus that the farmer, etc.
Reaps his barley and wheat.

5. Shall I show you how the farmer, etc.
Threshes barley and wheat.

6. Look 'tis thus, thus that the farmer, etc.
Threshes barley and wheat.

As this song is sung, the children imitate the farmer sowing, reaping and threshing his wheat.

The Farmyard

OLD LONDON FOLK SONG

Lively
mf
1. Up was I on fa-ther's farm On a May-day morn-ing
Feed-ing of my fa-ther's cows On a May-day morn-ing
2. Up was I on fa-ther's farm On a May-day morn-ing
Feed-ing of my fa-ther's goats On a May-day morn-ing
1 (Omit second time)
2
ear - ly, ear - ly. With a moo, moo here, and a moo, moo there,
ear - ly, ear - ly. With a nan, nan here, and a nan, nan there,
Here a moo, there a moo, here a pret-ty moo;
Here a nan, there a nan, here a pret-ty nan;
Six pret-ty maids, come gang a-long o' me To the mer-ry green fields and the farm-yard.

This song may be continued by using the names of other animals and the sounds they make as sheep (baa-baa), ducks (quack-quack).

A Capital Ship

OLD ENGLISH FOLK SONG

Spirited
1. A cap-i-tal ship for an o - cean trip Was the Walloping Win-dow Blind! No
2. The bo'-swain's mate was ver-y se-date, Yet fond of a-muse-ment too; He
3. The cap-tain sat on the commodore's hat, And dined in a roy - al way, Off
4. All nau-ti-cal pride we laid a-side, And we ran the ves-sel a - shore On the
5. On Rug - bug bark, from morn till dark, We dined till we all had grown Un -
wind that blew dis - mayed her crew, Or trou-bled the cap - tain's mind. The
play'd hop-scotch with the starboard watch, While the captain tickled the crew. And the
toast-ed pigs and pickles and figs, And gun-ner-y bread each day. And the
Gul-i-by Isles where the Poo-poo smiles, And the rub - bly Up - dugs roar. And we
commonly shrunk, when a Chinese junk Came up from the Tor-ri-bly zone. She was
man at the wheel was made to feel Con - tempt for the wild-est blow-ow-ow, Tho' it
gun-ner we had was ap-par-ent-ly mad, For he sat on the aft-er rai-ai-ail, And
cook was Dutch and be-haved as such, For the di - et he gave the crew-ew-ew, Was a
sat on the edge of a sand - y ledge And shot at the whistling bee-ee-ee; And the
chubby and square, but we didn't much care, So we cheer-i-ly put out to sea-ea-ea; And we
of - ten ap-peared, when the gale had clear'd, That he'd been in his bunk be - low.
fired sa-lutes with the cap - tain's boots, In the teeth of the boom-ing gale!
number of tons of hot cross buns Served up with sug-ar and glue.
cin-na-mon bats wore wa-ter proof hats As they dipped in the shin - y sea.
left all the crew of the junk to chew On the bark of the Rug - bug tree.

A Capital Ship–Continued
CHORUS
Then blow, ye winds, heigh ho! A-rov-ing I will go! I'll stay no more on
Eng-land's shore, So let the mu-sic play-ay-ay! I'm off for the morn-ing train! I'll
cross the raging main! I'm off to my love with a box-ing glove, Ten thousand miles a-way!
Swing Low, Sweet Chariot
NEGRO "SPIRITUAL"
hm
CHORUS
LEADER
Swing low sweet chariot, Com-in' fo' to car-ry me home, Swing low sweet chariot,
hm
hm
hm
CHORUS
Fine.
LEADER
CHORUS
Com-in' fo' to car-ry me home.
1. I looked o-ver Jordan and what did I see,
2. If you get there be-fore I do,
3. The brightest day that ev-er I saw,
4. I'm some-times up and some-times down,
Comin' fo' to
LEADER
CHORUS
car-ry me home,
A band of angels com-in' after me,
Tell all my friends I'm com-in' too,
When Jesus wash'd my sins a-way,
But still my soul feels heav'n-ly bound,
Comin' fo' to car-ry me home.

TRANSLATION
The Little Dustman
FOLK SONG OF THE NETHERLANDS
Arr. by JOHANNES BRAHMS
Moderately quick
1. The flow'rets all sleep sound-ly Beneath the moon's bright ray; They nod their heads to-geth - er And dream the night away. The rust'ling trees wave to and fro, And murmur soft and low. Sleep on, sleep on, Sleep on, my lit-tle one.
2. Now see, the lit-tle dust-man At the window shows his head And looks for an-y chil-dren Who ought to be in bed; And as each weary one he spies, Throws dust into his eyes. Sleep on, sleep on, Sleep on, my lit-tle one.
p
1
2
Adapted by JANE B. WALTERS
The Patriots
THÜRINGIAN FOLK SONG
1. 'Tis here we are pledging with heart and with hand, Full measure of de - vo-tion to thee, our na-tive land; Full measure of de - vo - tion to thee, our na-tive land.
2. Now all join the cho - rus, let u - nion a - bide, The flag is waving o'er us for which our fa-thers died; The flag is waving o'er us for which our fa-thers died.
3. O star-ry Old Glo - ry of red, white and blue! We love thy honored sto-ry; to thee we'll e'er be true; We love thy honored sto - ry; to thee we'll e'er be true.

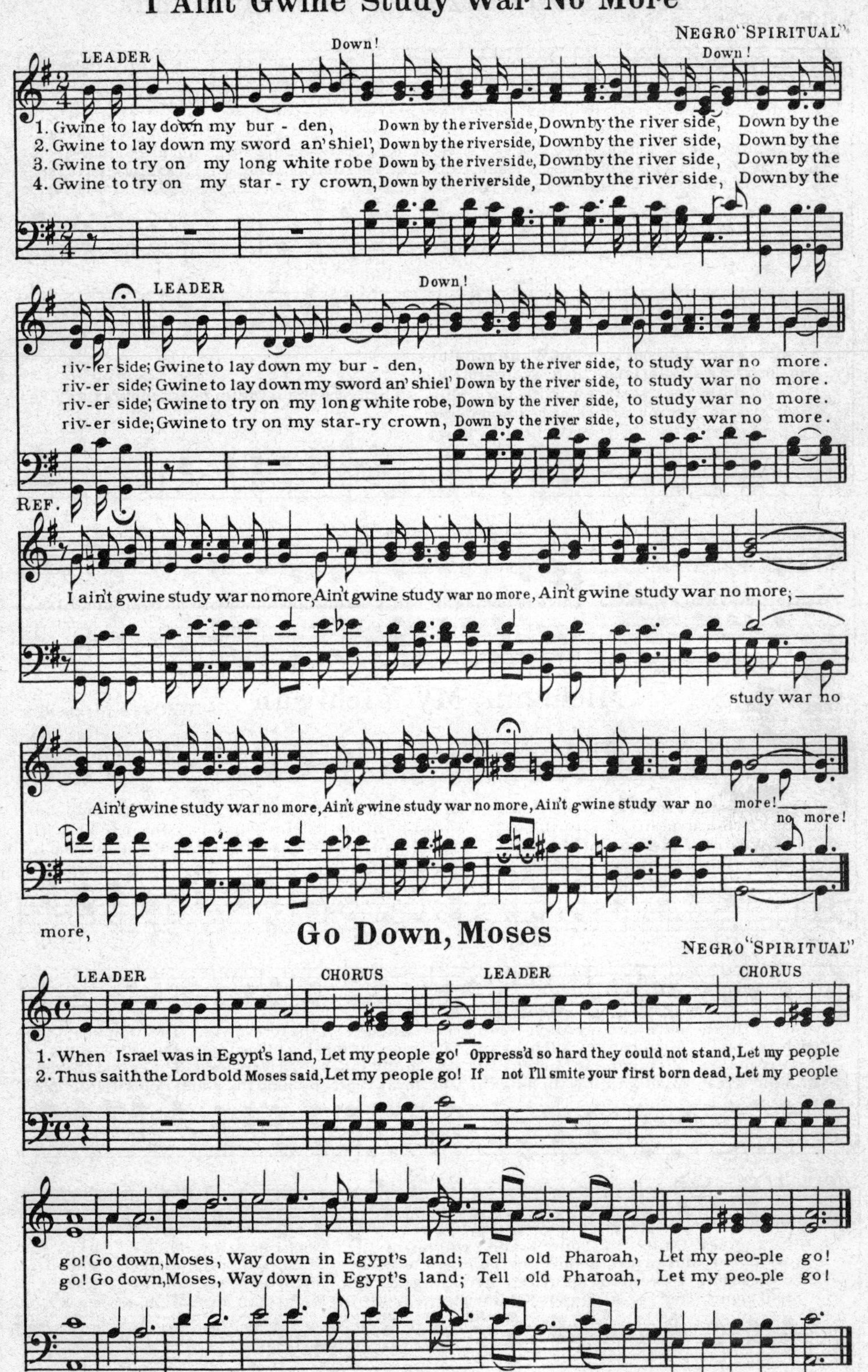
97
I Ain't Gwine Study War No More
Negro "Spiritual"
Leader
Down!
Down!
1. Gwine to lay down my bur - den, Down by the riverside, Down by the river side, Down by the
2. Gwine to lay down my sword an' shiel', Down by the riverside, Down by the river side, Down by the
3. Gwine to try on my long white robe Down by the riverside, Down by the river side, Down by the
4. Gwine to try on my star - ry crown, Down by the riverside, Down by the river side, Down by the
Leader
Down!
riv-er side; Gwine to lay down my bur - den, Down by the river side, to study war no more.
riv-er side; Gwine to lay down my sword an' shiel' Down by the river side, to study war no more.
riv-er side; Gwine to try on my long white robe, Down by the river side, to study war no more.
riv-er side; Gwine to try on my star-ry crown, Down by the river side, to study war no more.
Ref.
I ain't gwine study war no more, Ain't gwine study war no more, Ain't gwine study war no more;
study war no
Ain't gwine study war no more, Ain't gwine study war no more, Ain't gwine study war no more!
no more!
more,
Go Down, Moses
Negro "Spiritual"
Leader
Chorus
Leader
Chorus
1. When Israel was in Egypt's land, Let my people go! Oppress'd so hard they could not stand, Let my people
2. Thus saith the Lord bold Moses said, Let my people go! If not I'll smite your first born dead, Let my people
go! Go down, Moses, Way down in Egypt's land; Tell old Pharoah, Let my peo-ple go!
go! Go down, Moses, Way down in Egypt's land; Tell old Pharoah, Let my peo-ple go!

There Are Many Flags In Many Lands

M.H. HOWLISTON

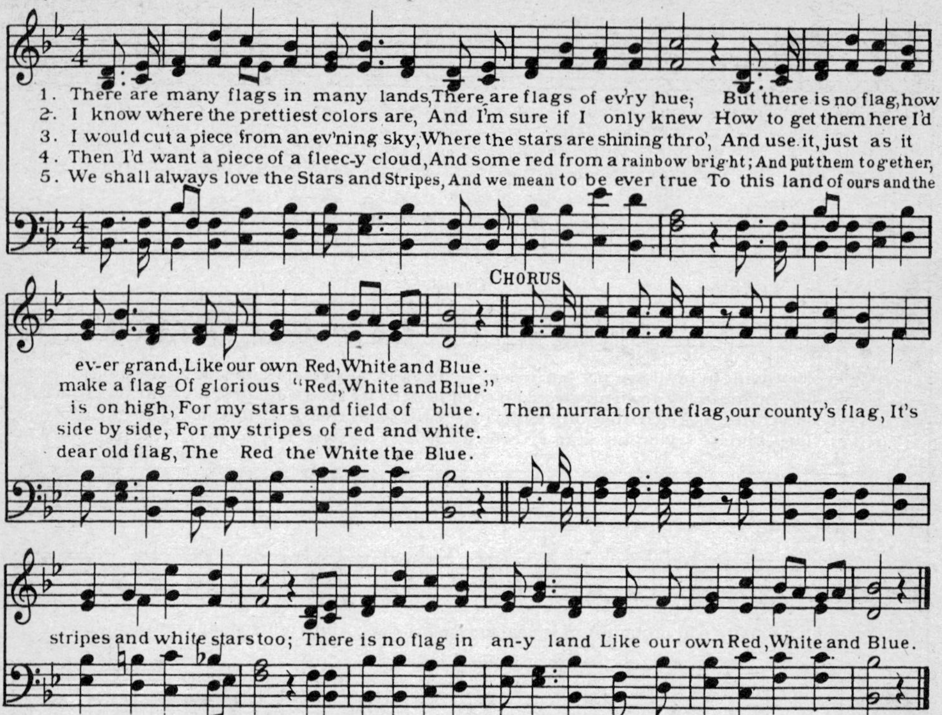

1. There are many flags in many lands, There are flags of ev'ry hue; But there is no flag, how
2. I know where the prettiest colors are, And I'm sure if I only knew How to get them here I'd
3. I would cut a piece from an ev'ning sky, Where the stars are shining thro', And use it, just as it
4. Then I'd want a piece of a fleec-y cloud, And some red from a rainbow bright; And put them together,
5. We shall always love the Stars and Stripes, And we mean to be ever true To this land of ours and the

CHORUS

ev-er grand, Like our own Red, White and Blue.
make a flag Of glorious "Red, White and Blue."
is on high, For my stars and field of blue. Then hurrah for the flag, our county's flag, It's
side by side, For my stripes of red and white.
dear old flag, The Red the White the Blue.

stripes and white stars too; There is no flag in an-y land Like our own Red, White and Blue.

Michigan, My Michigan

DOUGLAS MALLOCH W. OTTO MIESSNER

1. A song to thee, fair State of mine, Mich-i-gan, my Michi-gan; But greater song than
2. I sing a State of all the best, Mich-i-gan, my Michi-gan; I sing a State with
3. How fair the bosom of thy lakes, Mich-i-gan, my Michi-gan; What mel-o-dy each
4. Thou rich in wealth that makes a State, Mich-i-gan, my Michi-gan; Thou great in things that

this is thine, Michigan, my Mich-i-gan; The whisper of the forest tree, The thunder of the
rich-es bless'd, Michigan, my Mich-i-gan; Thy mines unmask a hidden store, But richer thy his-
riv-er makes Michigan, my Mich-i-gan; As to thy lakes thy rivers tend, Thy exiled children
make us great, Michigan, my Mich-i-gan; Our loyal voices sound thy claim Upon the golden

in-land sea, U-nite in one grand sympho-ny Of Michi-gan, my Mich-i-gan.
to-ric lore, More great the love thy build-ers bore, Oh, Michi-gan, my Mich-i-gan.
to thee send De-vo-tion that shall nev-er end, Oh, Michi-gan, my Mich-i-gan.
roll of Fame Our loy-al hands shall write the name Of Michi-gan, my Mich-i-gan.

The Maple Leaf Forever

A. L.
ALEXANDER MUIR
With spirit
1. In days of yore, from Britain's shore, Wolfe the dauntless he-ro came, And planted firm Bri-tan-ia's flag, On Ca-na-da's fair do-main; Here may it wave, our boast and pride, And join in love to-geth-er, The This-tle, Shamrock, Rose entwine The Maple Leaf for-ev-er.
2. At Queens-town Heights, and Lundy's Lane, Our brave fa-thers side by side, For freedom, homes, and loved ones dear, Firmly stood and no-bly died; And those dear rights which they maintain'd We swear to yield them never, Our watch word ev-er-more shall be, The Maple Leaf for-ev-er.
3. Our fair Do-min-ion now ex-tends From Cape Race to Nootka Sound, May peace for-ev-er be our lot, And plen-teous store a-bound; And may those ties of love be ours, Which dis-cord can-not sever, And flour-ish green o'er Freedom's home, The Maple Leaf for-ev-er.
4. On Mer-ry Eng-land's far famed land May kind Heaven sweetly smile, God bless Old Scotland ev-er-more, And Ire-land's Em-'rald Isle; Then swell the song both loud and long, Till rocks and for-est quiv-er, God save our King, and Heaven bless The Maple Leaf for-ev-er.
CHORUS
mf
The Ma-ple Leaf our em-blem dear, The Ma-ple Leaf for-ev-er, God save our King and Heav-en bless The Ma-ple Leaf for-ev-er.
f

March Of The Men Of Harlech

Welsh Poem translated
by William Duthie

Harmonized
by Joseph Barnby
WELSH AIR

mf *March time*

1. Men of Har-lech! hon-or calls us, No proud Saxon e'er ap-palls us!
2. Tho' our mothers may be weep-ing, Tho' our sisters may be keep-ing

On we march! whate'er befalls us, Nev-er shall we fly! *rit.* Forward, lightly
Watch for some who now are sleeping On the bat-tle-field, Still the trumpet's

cresc.

bound-ing, To the trumpet's sounding; Forward ev-er, backward, ne'er, The
bray-ing Sounds on, ev-er say-ing, Let each bow-man pierce a foe, And

haughty foe as-tound-ing; Fight for father, sis-ter, mother, Each is bound to
nev-er stop the slay-ing, Till in-vaders learn to fear us, And no Saxon

ff

each as brother; And with faith in one an-oth-er, We will win or die!
lin-ger near us; Men of Wales! our God doth hear us, Never will we yield!

Dip, Boys, Dip The Oar

F. SARONA

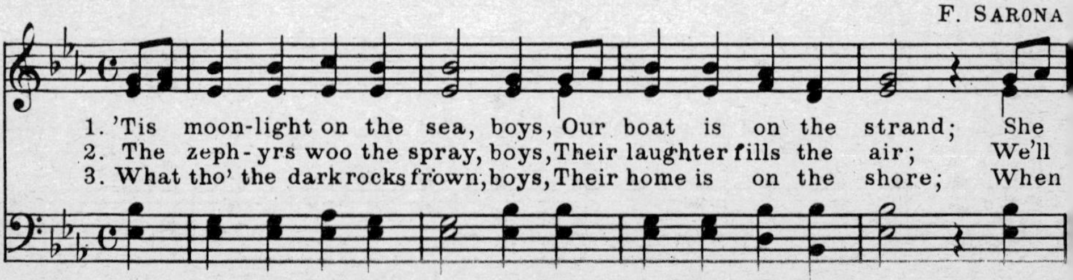

1. 'Tis moon-light on the sea, boys, Our boat is on the strand; She
2. The zeph-yrs woo the spray, boys, Their laughter fills the air; We'll
3. What tho' the dark rocks frown, boys, Their home is on the shore; When

Dip, Boys, Dip The Oar—Continued
CHORUS
bids us all be free, boys, And seek a fair-er land.
bid them wake our song, boys, And steal away our care.
fairer lands ap- pear, boys, Our dangers will be o'er.
Dip, boys, dip the oar,
Bid farewell to the dusky shore; Freedom ours shall be, As we cross the deep blue sea.
Woodman, Spare That Tree
GEORGE POPE MORRIS
HENRY RUSSELL
1. Wood-man, spare that tree! Touch not a sin-gle bough; In youth it sheltered
2. That old fa-mil-iar tree, Its glo-ry and re-nown Are spread o'er land and
3. When but an i-dle boy, I sought its grateful shade; In all their gushing
4. My heart-strings round thee cling, Close as thy bark, old friend! Here shall the wildbird
me, And I'll pro-tect it now; 'Twas my fore-fa-ther's hand, That
sea, And would'st thou hew it down? Wood-man, for-bear thy stroke! Cut
joy, Here, too, my sis-ters played; My moth-er kissed me here; My
sing, And still thy branches bend. Old tree, the storm thou'lt brave, And,
placed it near his cot, There, woodman, let it stand, Thy axe shall harm it not!
not its earth-bound ties; Oh! spare that a-ged oak, Now tow-'ring to the skies.
fa-ther pressed my hand, For-give this foolish tear, But let that old oak stand!
woodman, leave the spot; While I've a hand to save, Thy axe shall harm it not!

Santa Lucia
With swinging motion
Neapolitan Boat Song
1. Now 'neath the silver moon Ocean is glowing, O'er the calm bil-low Soft winds are blowing;
2. When o'er thy waters Light winds are playing, Thy spell can soothe us, All care al-lay-ing;
Here balmy breezes blow, Pure joys invite us, And as we gently row, All things delight us.
To thee, sweet Na-po-li, What charms are given, Where smiles creation, Toil blest by heaven.
Chorus
Hark, how the sailor's cry Joyous-ly echoes nigh: San-ta Lu-ci-a! Santa Lu-ci-a,
Home of fair Po-e-sy, Realm of pure Harmony, San-ta Lu-ci-a! Santa Lu-ci-a!
In The Gloaming
Meta Orred
Annie F. Harrison
Slowly
1. In the gloaming oh, my darling! when the lights are dim and low, And the qui-et
2. In the gloaming oh, my darling! think not bit-ter-ly of me! Though I passed a-
shad-ows, fall-ing, soft-ly come and soft-ly go, When the winds are sob-bing
way in si-lence, left you lone-ly, set you free, For my heart was crushed with

In The Gloaming—Continued
faintly with a gen-tle, unknown woe, Will you think of me and love me, As you did once
longing; what had been could never be. It was best to leave you thus, dear, Best for you an
1
2
rall
cresc.
long a-go?
best for me. It was best to leave you thus, Best for you and best for me.
Last Night The Nightingale Woke Me
Moderately
HALFDAN KJERULF
1. Last night the night-in-gale woke me, Last night when all was still; It
2. I think of you in the day-time, I dream of you by night, I
3. O think not I can for-get you; I could not tho' I would; I
sang in the gold-en moon-light, From out the wood-land hill, I
wake, and would you were here, love, And tears are blinding my sight, I
see you in all a-round me, The stream, the night, the wood, The
o-pened my win-dow so gent-ly, I looked on the dreaming dew, And
hear a low breath in the lime-tree, The wind is float-ing thro' And
flow-ers that slum-ber so gent-ly, The stars a-bove the blue, O
oh, the bird, my dar-ling, Was sing-ing, sing-ing of you, of you.
oh, the night, my dar-ling, Is sigh-ing, sigh-ing for you, for you.
heav'n it-self, my dar-ling, Is pray-ing, pray-ing for you, for you.

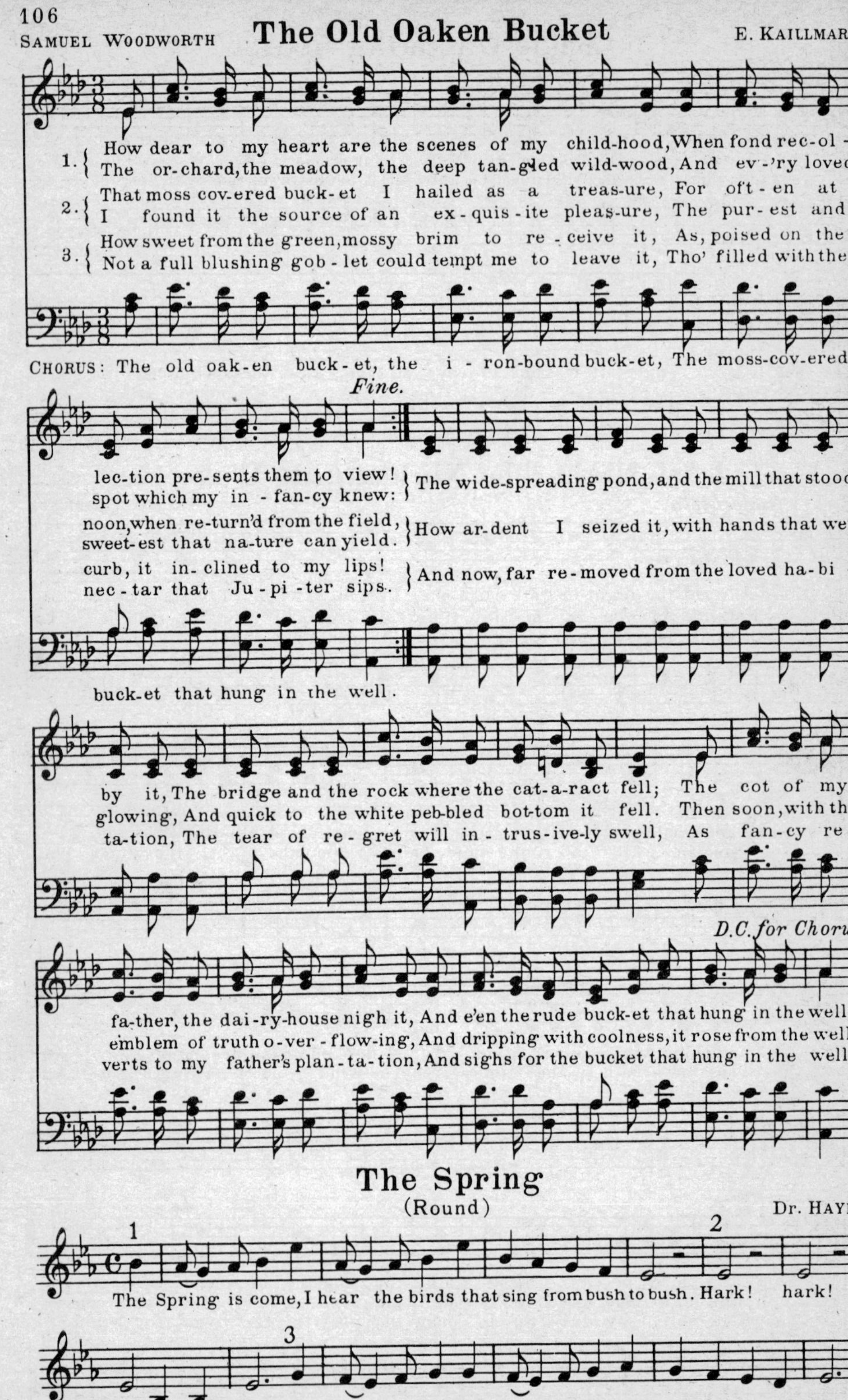
SAMUEL WOODWORTH
The Old Oaken Bucket
E. KAILLMAR
1. How dear to my heart are the scenes of my child-hood, When fond rec-ol - lec-tion pre-sents them to view!
The or-chard, the meadow, the deep tan-gled wild-wood, And ev-'ry loved spot which my in - fan-cy knew:
2. That moss cov-ered buck-et I hailed as a treas-ure, For oft - en at noon, when re-turn'd from the field,
I found it the source of an ex-quis - ite pleas-ure, The pur - est and sweet-est that na-ture can yield.
3. How sweet from the green, mossy brim to re - ceive it, As, poised on the curb, it in- clined to my lips!
Not a full blushing gob - let could tempt me to leave it, Tho' filled with the nec-tar that Ju-pi -ter sips.
CHORUS: The old oak-en buck - et, the i - ron-bound buck-et, The moss-cov-ered buck-et that hung in the well.
Fine.
The wide-spreading pond, and the mill that stood by it, The bridge and the rock where the cat-a-ract fell; The cot of my fa-ther, the dai-ry-house nigh it, And e'en the rude buck-et that hung in the well
How ar-dent I seized it, with hands that were glowing, And quick to the white peb-bled bot-tom it fell. Then soon, with the emblem of truth o-ver - flow-ing, And dripping with coolness, it rose from the well
And now, far re-moved from the loved ha-bi - ta-tion, The tear of re - gret will in - trus-ive-ly swell, As fan-cy re - verts to my father's plan - ta - tion, And sighs for the bucket that hung in the well
D.C. for Chorus
The Spring
(Round)
Dr. HAYES
1 2 3
The Spring is come, I hear the birds that sing from bush to bush. Hark! hark! I hear them sing. The lin - net and the lit - tle wren, the black bird and the thrush

Those Evening Bells
Thomas Moore
Moderately
Fine.
1. Those evening bells! those eve-ning bells! How man-y a tale their mu-sic tells,
2. Those joy-ous hours have passed a-way; And man-y a heart that then was gay,
3. And so 'twill be when I am gone, That tune-ful peal will still ring on,
D. C.
Of youth and home, and that sweet time When last I heard their soothing chime.
With-in the tomb now dark-ly dwells, And hears no more those evening bells.
While oth-er bards shall walk these dells, And sing your praise, sweet evening bells.
When The Swallows Homeward Fly
Carl Herlossohn
Franz Abt
1. When the swallows homeward fly, When the ro - ses scatter'd lie, When from
2. When the white swan southward roves, To seek at noon the orange groves, When the
3. Hush, my heart! why thus complain? Thou must, too, thy woes contain, Tho' on
nei-ther hill nor dale Chants the sil-v'ry nightingale; In these words my bleeding
red tints of the west Prove the sun has gone to rest; In these words my bleeding
earth no more we rove, Loud-ly breathing words of love; Thou, my heart, must find re-
heart Would to thee its grief im-part, When I thus thy im - age lose,
heart Would to thee its grief im-part, When I thus thy im - age lose,
lief, Yield-ing to these words belief; I shall see thy form a - gain,
Can I, ah, can I e'er know re-pose, Can I ah, can I e'er know repose?
Can I, ah, can I e'er know re-pose, Can I ah, can I e'er know repose?
Though to-day we part a-gain, Though to - day we part a-gain.

Go To Sleep, Lena Darling

(Emmet's Lullaby)

J.K.E. J.K. EMMET

1. Close your eyes, Le - na, my darling, While I sing your lul-la - by; Fear thou no
2. Bright be the morn-ing, my darling, When you ope your eyes Sunbeams glow all
danger, Le - na, Move not, dear Le - na, my darling, For your brother watches
'round you, Le - na, Peace be with thee, love, my darling, Blue and cloudless be the
nigh you, Lena dear. Angels guide thee, Le - na dear, my darling, Noth-ing e - vil
sky for Lena dear. Birds sing their bright songs for thee, my darling, Full of sweetest
can come near; Brightest flowers blow for thee, Darling ba-by dear to me.
mel - o - dy; An-gels ev - er hov-er near, Darling ba-by dear to me.
CHORUS
Go to sleep, go to sleep, my ba - by, my ba - by, my ba - by,
Go to sleep, my ba-by, ba - by, oh, bye, Go to sleep, Le-na sleep

The Loreley

HEINRICH HEINE — FRIEDRICH SILCHER

With a moderately quick motion
p
1. I know not what it pre - sa - ges, That
2. The most beau - ti - ful maid is re - clin - ing On the
3. It seiz - es with wild - est yearn - ing, The
I am so sad to - day; A leg - end of for - mer
cliff, so won - drous fair; Her glo - ri - ous jew - els are
boat-man, entranc'd in his skiff; He sees not the treach-er - ous
a - ges Will not from my tho'ts a - way. The
shin - ing, She is comb - ing her gold - en hair; With a
break - ers, He gaz - es a - lone on the cliff. And
dim. e rit.
air is cool and it dar - kles, The Rhine flows calm - ly on, The
gold - en comb she combs it, And sings a song there - by, That
soon will the waves en - gulf them, Both boat and boat - man strong, For
a tempo
rit.
peak of the moun - tain sparkles In the glow of the eve - ning sun.
hrills with its mys - tic mean - ing, And pow - er - ful mel - o - dy.
thus in her toils hath she bound them, The Lore - ley with her song.

The Little Brown Church In The Vale
W. S. P.
WILLIAM S. PITTS
1. There's a church in the valley by the wild-wood, No lov - li - er place in the dale;
2. How sweet on a bright Sabbath morning To list to the clear ringing bell;
No spot is so dear to my child-hood As the lit - tle brown church in the vale.
Its tones so sweet - ly are call - ing, O come to the church in the vale.
rit.
a tempo
Come to the church in the wildwood, O come to the church in the
O come, come, come, come, come, come, come, come, come, come, come, come, come, come, come, come,
rit.
dale;
After 2nd verse, repeat Cho. pp
come, come, come, No spot is so dear to my child-hood As the lit - tle brown church in the vale.
Come, With Thy Lute
1. Come, with thy lute, to the fountain; Sing me a song of the mountain; Sing of the hap - py and
2. Come, where the zephyrs are straying, Where, mid the flowerbuds play-ing, Rambles the blithe summer
3. Why should we droop in our sadness? Nature, her promise of gladness Sheds o-ver land and o'er
free, There while the ray is de - clin - ing, While its last ro - ses are shining, Sweet shall our
bee; Let the lone churl, in his sorrow, He who de-spairs of the morrow, Far to his
sea; Come, bring thy lute to the fountain, Sing, love, a song of the mountain; Sweet shall our

Come With Thy Lute—Continued

mel-o-dies be, Un-der the broad lin-den tree, Under the broad lin-den tree.
sol-i-tude flee, Un-der the dark cy-press tree, Under the dark cy-press tree.
mel-o-dies be, Un-der the broad lin-den tree, Under the broad lin-den tree.

Un-der the lin-den tree. Under the lin-den tree.

Graduation Song

EORGE COOPER — ANCIENT MELODY

Moderately quick

1. Our school-days now are past and gone, And yet we fond-ly lin-ger here; For sweet each joy that we have known: 'Tis sad to part from comrades dear. The world before us bright-ly lies, Yet here fond mem'ry loves to dwell; With saddened hearts and dew-y eyes We bid to all a sweet fare-well! Fare-well! Fare-well! We bid to all a sweet fare-well!

2. Long will our hearts re-call each joy That bound us in sweet friendship here; For time can nev-er-more de-stroy The light of mem-'ry burn-ing clear. Of oth-er scenes and oth-er cares Our lips must now their story tell; Each heart your ten-der mem-'ry shares, Teach-ers and comrades, now fare-well! Fare-well! Fare-well! Teach-ers and com-rades, now fare-well!

"Ye Olde Folkes' Concertte"

The songs "Revolutionary Tea," "Cousin Jedediah" and "Sound the Loud Timbrel" are examples of those which may be used to advantage in an Old Folks Concert. Programs of this type, made up of songs and recitations selected from among those popular in the days of the old time "Singing School," with the performers appropriately costumed, can be given in any community and are great fun. The more elderly people enjoy them because they bring back memories of an institution which, like the spelling match and husking bee, was important from a social standpoint. The younger people and children will be entertained by taking part in a program similar to one in which their grandparents often participated.

Revolutionary Tea

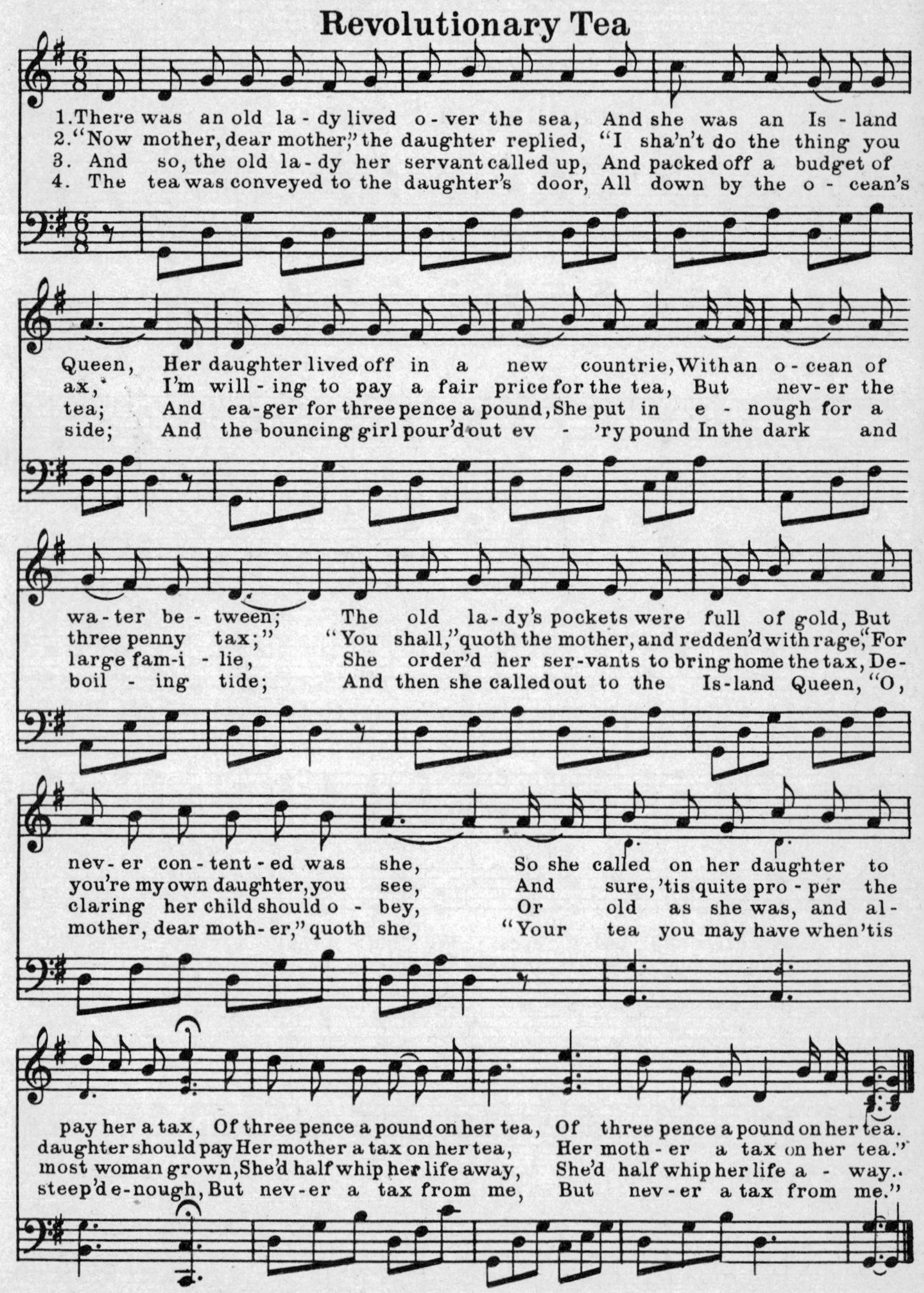
1. There was an old la-dy lived o-ver the sea, And she was an Is-land
2. "Now mother, dear mother," the daughter replied, "I sha'n't do the thing you
3. And so, the old la-dy her servant called up, And packed off a budget of
4. The tea was conveyed to the daughter's door, All down by the o-cean's
Queen, Her daughter lived off in a new countrie, With an o-cean of
ax," I'm will-ing to pay a fair price for the tea, But nev-er the
tea; And ea-ger for three pence a pound, She put in e-nough for a
side; And the bouncing girl pour'd out ev-'ry pound In the dark and
wa-ter be-tween; The old la-dy's pockets were full of gold, But
three penny tax;" "You shall," quoth the mother, and redden'd with rage, "For
large fam-i-lie, She order'd her ser-vants to bring home the tax, De-
boil-ing tide; And then she called out to the Is-land Queen, "O,
nev-er con-tent-ed was she, So she called on her daughter to
you're my own daughter, you see, And sure, 'tis quite pro-per the
claring her child should o-bey, Or old as she was, and al-
mother, dear moth-er," quoth she, "Your tea you may have when 'tis
pay her a tax, Of three pence a pound on her tea, Of three pence a pound on her tea.
daughter should pay Her mother a tax on her tea, Her moth-er a tax on her tea."
most woman grown, She'd half whip her life away, She'd half whip her life a-way..
steep'd e-nough, But nev-er a tax from me, But nev-er a tax from me."

Cousin Jedediah

H. S. Thompson

1. Oh! Jacob, get the cows home and put them in the pen, For the cousins are a-coming to
2. Now, O-bed, wash your face, boy, and tallow up your shoes, While I go to see Aunt Betty, and
3. And, Job, you peel the onions, and wash and fix the 'taters, We'll have them on the table in those
4. Tell Josh to put the colt in the double seated chaise, Let him just card down the cattle, give
see us all a-gain; The dowdy's in the pan, and the tur-key's on the fire,
tell her all the news; And, Kit-ty, slick your hair, and put on your Sunday gown,
shin-y painted waiters; Put on your bran new boots, and those trousers with the straps
them a lit-tle hay; I'll wear my nice new bell-crown I bought of old U-ri-ah,
And we all must get read-y for Cous-in Jed-e-di-ah.
For Cousin Jed-e-di-ah comes right from Bos-ton town.
Aunt So-phia'll take a shine to you, if you look real slick, per-haps.
And I guess we'll as-ton-ish our Cous-in Jed-e-di-ah
CHORUS
And Az-a-riah, And Aunt Sophia,
Cousin Jed-e-di-ah, There's Hezekiah,
And Jed-e-di-ah,
All com-ing here to tea; Oh! won't we have a jol-ly time, Oh!
won't we have a jol-ly time! Je-ru-sha, put the ket-tle on, We'll all take tea.

114
Sound The Loud Timbrel
With spirit
CHARLES AVISON
f
With spirit
1. Sound the loud tim-brel o'er E-gypt's dark sea; Je - ho - vah has tri-umph'd His peo-ple are free; Sing, for the pride of the ty - rant is bro - ken; His chari-ots, His horse-men all splen-did and brave; How vain was their boast-ing, the
2. Praise to the con-quer-or, Praise to the Lord: His word was our ar-row, His breath was our sword Who shall re-turn to tell E - gypt the sto - ry Of those she sent forth in the hour of her pride? The Lord hath look'd out from His

Sound The Loud Timbrel–Continued

Lord hath but spoken, And chariots and horsemen are sunk in the wave.
pil-lar of glo-ry, And all her brave thousands are dash'd in the tide.
Sound the loud tim-brel o'er E-gypt's dark sea; ____ Je-ho-vah has tri-umph'd, His
Praise to the Con-quer-or; Praise to the Lord: ____ His word was our ar-row — His
1
2
CODA
f
peo-ple are free, peo-ple are free, His peo-ple are free, His peo-ple are free.
breath was our sword, breath was our sword, His breath was our sword His breath was our sword.
f
tr

I Cannot Sing The Old Songs
Mrs. C.B.
Mrs. CHARLES BARNARD
Slowly
1. I can-not sing the old songs, I sang long years a-go, For heart and voice would fail me, And fool-ish tears would flow; For by-gone hours come o'er my heart, with each fa-mil-iar strain. I can-not sing the old songs, Or dream those dreams a-gain, I can-not sing the old songs, Or dream those dreams a-gain.
2. I can-not sing the old songs, Their charm is sad and deep; Their melodies would wa-ken Old sor-rows from their sleep, And tho' all un-for-got-ten still, and sad-ly sweet they be, I can-not sing the old songs, They are too dear to me; I can-not sing the old songs, They are too dear to me.
3. I can-not sing the old songs, For vis-ions come a-gain Of gold-en dreams de-part-ed And years of wea-ry pain, Per-haps when earthly fet-ters shall have set my spir-it free, My voice may know the old songs, For all e-ter-ni-ty, My voice may know the old songs, For all e-ter-ni-ty.
Good-night, Ladies
Male Quartette
COLLEGE SONG
1. Good-night, ladies! Good-night, ladies! Good-night, ladies! We're going to leave you now.
2. Fare-well, ladies! Fare-well, ladies! Fare-well, ladies! We're going to leave you now.
3. Sweet dreams, ladies! Sweet dreams, ladies! Sweet dreams, ladies! We're going to leave you now.
Mer-ri-ly we roll along, Roll along, roll along, Merrily we roll along, Over the dark blue sea.

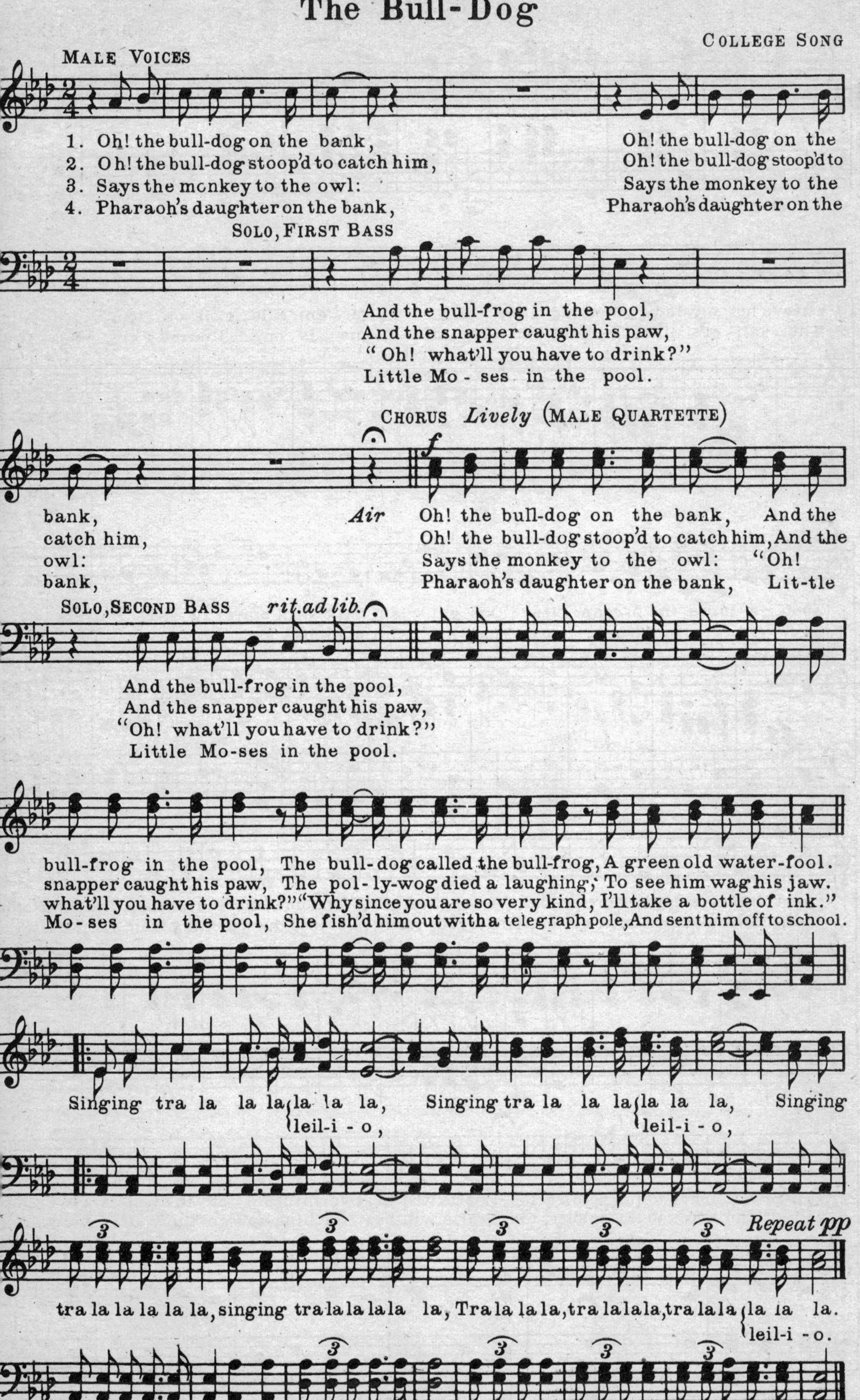
The Bull-Dog
College Song
Male Voices
1. Oh! the bull-dog on the bank,
2. Oh! the bull-dog stoop'd to catch him,
3. Says the monkey to the owl:
4. Pharaoh's daughter on the bank,
Oh! the bull-dog on the bank,
Oh! the bull-dog stoop'd to catch him,
Says the monkey to the owl:
Pharaoh's daughter on the bank,
Solo, First Bass
And the bull-frog in the pool,
And the snapper caught his paw,
"Oh! what'll you have to drink?"
Little Mo - ses in the pool.
Solo, Second Bass
rit. ad lib.
And the bull-frog in the pool,
And the snapper caught his paw,
"Oh! what'll you have to drink?"
Little Mo-ses in the pool.
Chorus Lively (Male Quartette)
f
Air
Oh! the bull-dog on the bank, And the bull-frog in the pool, The bull-dog called the bull-frog, A green old water-fool.
Oh! the bull-dog stoop'd to catch him, And the snapper caught his paw, The pol-ly-wog died a laughing, To see him wag his jaw.
Says the monkey to the owl: "Oh! what'll you have to drink?" "Why since you are so very kind, I'll take a bottle of ink."
Pharaoh's daughter on the bank, Lit-tle Mo-ses in the pool, She fish'd him out with a telegraph pole, And sent him off to school.
Singing tra la la la la la la, Singing tra la la la la la la, Singing
leil-i - o, leil-i - o,
tra la la la la la, singing tra la la la la la, Tra la la la, tra la la la, tra la la la la la.
leil-i - o.
Repeat pp

Sailing
G. F.
GODFREY MARKS
f
1. Y'heave ho! my lads, the wind blows free, A pleas-ant gale is on our lee; And soon a-cross the o-cean clear Our gal-lant bark shall brave-ly steer. But ere we part from Freedom's shores to-night, A song we'll sing for home and beauty bright. Then here's to the sail-or and here's to the soldier, too, Hearts will beat for him up-on the waters blue.
2. The sail-or's life is bold and free, His home is on the roll-ing sea; And nev-er heart more true or brave Than his who launches on the wave; A-far he speeds in distant climes to roam, With joyous song he rides the sparkling foam. Then here's to the sail-or and here's to the soldier, too, Hearts will beat for him up-on the waters blue.

Sailing—Continued
CHORUS
GODFREY MARKS
Sail-ing, sail-ing, o-ver the bound-ing main. For man-y a storm-y
wind shall blow ere Jack comes home a-gain! Sail-ing, sail-ing, o-ver the
bounding main, For man-y a storm-y wind shall blow ere Jack comes home a-gain!
De Bezem
(Round)
This Dutch round is great fun, whether the singers can pronounce the words correctly or not. The phonetic pronunciation, with translation is given below.
FROM THE NETHERLANDS
DUTCH WORDS: De be-zem, de be-zem, Wat doe je er mee, Wat doe je er mee?
PRONUNCIATION: Dă bay-sŭm, dă bay-sŭm, Wat doo yă air may, Wat doo yă air may?
TRANSLATION: The broom, the broom, What do you with it, What do you with it?
Wij ve-gen er mee, Wij ve-gen er mee, De vloer aan, de vloer aan.
Way fay-gan air may, Way fay-gan air may, Da fluur on, da fluur on.
We sweep with it, We sweep with it, The floor up, the floor up.
Three Blind Mice
(Round)
Three blind mice, Three blind mice, See how they run, See how they
run! They all ran af-ter the farmer's wife, She cut off their tails with a
carving knife; Did ev-er you see such a thing in your life, As three blind mice?

Jingle, Bells

J. P. — J. PIERPONT

Quickly

1. — Dashing thro' the snow In a one horse open sleigh, — O'er the fields we go, — Laughing all the way; — Bells on bob-tail ring, — Making spirits bright, What fun it is to ride and sing A sleighing song to-night!

2. A day or two ago I — thought I'd take a ride, And soon Miss Fannie Bright Was seated by my side; The horse was lean and lank, Misfortune seem'd his lot, He got into a drifted bank, And we, we got upsot.

3. — Now the ground is white, — Go it while you're young, — Take the girls to-night, And sing this sleighing song; Just get a bob-tailed nag, Two-forty for his speed, Then hitch him to an open sleigh, And crack! you'll take the lead.

CHORUS (*Accompanied by jingling glasses*)

Jingle, bells! jingle, bells! Jingle all the way! Oh, what fun it is to ride

1. In a one-horse open sleigh!

2. In a one-horse open sleigh!

My Bonnie
College Song
1. My Bon-nie is o-ver the o-cean, My Bon-nie is o-ver the sea, My Bon-nie is o-ver the o-cean, O bring back my Bonnie to me.
2. O blow, ye winds, o-ver the o-cean, And blow, ye winds, over the sea, O blow, ye winds, o-ver the o-cean, And bring back my Bonnie to me.
3. Last night as I lay on my pil-low, Last night as I lay on my bed, Last night as I lay on my pil-low, I dream'd that my Bonnie was dead.
4. The winds have blown over the ocean, The winds have blown over the sea, The winds have blown o-ver the o-cean, And bro't back my Bonnie to me.
Chorus
Bring back, bring back, Bring back my Bonnie to me, to me; Bring back, bring back, O bring back my Bonnie to me.
Central Will Shine
(The name of any school may be substituted for "Central")
School Song
Male Quartette
Cen-tral will shine to-night, Central will shine, She'll shine in beauty bright All down the line,
Won't we look neat to night,
Dress'd up so fine;
When the sun goes down And the moon goes up
Central will shine.
Are You Sleeping?
(Round)
French Air
1
2
Are you sleep-ing, are you sleep-ing? Broth-er John, Broth-er John,
3
4
Morn-ing bells are ring-ing, Morning bells are ringing: Ding, ding, dong, ding, ding, dong.

Solomon Levi

COLLEGE SONG

My name is Sol-o-mon Le-vi And my store's on Sa-lem Street; That's
where to buy your coats and vests And ev-'ry-thing else that's neat;
Sec-ond hand-ed ul-ster-ettes And o-ver-coats so fine, For
Fine.
all the boys that trade with me at Hundred and for-ty-nine.
Tra-la-la-la-la-la-la.
O, Sol-o-mon Le-vi Tra-la-la-la-la.
Tra-la-la-la-la-la-la-la-la, D.S. al Fine.
Poor Sol-lie Le-vi, Tra-la-la-la-la-la-la-la-la, My
la-la, My

The Spanish Cavalier

V.D.H. WM. D. HENDRICKSON

1. A Span-ish Cav-a-lier stood in his re-treat, And
2. I'm off to the war, to the war I must go, To
3. And when the war is o'er, to you I'll re-turn, A-
on his gui-tar played a tune, dear; The mu-sic so sweet, Would
fight for my coun-try and you, dear; But if I should fall, In
gain to my coun-try and you, dear; But if I be slain, You may
oft-times re-peat The bless-ing of my coun-try and you, dear.
vain I would call, The bless-ing of my coun-try and you, dear.
seek me in vain, Up-on the bat-tle-field you will find me.
CHORUS
Oh, say, darling, say, when I'm far a-way, Some-times you may think of me, dear;
Bright sunny days will soon fade away, Re-member what I say, and be true, dear.

A Vocal Combat

"The Spanish Cavalier" and "Solomon Levi" may be sung simultaneously by two groups of singers. The groups should be of equal strength and each group rehearsed on its song until it can sing it well. Then, under some capable leader who will mark the rhythm with strongly accented beat, let the two groups sing the numbers together. There should be no attempt at piano accompaniment. Singers of all ages will enjoy the "stunt".

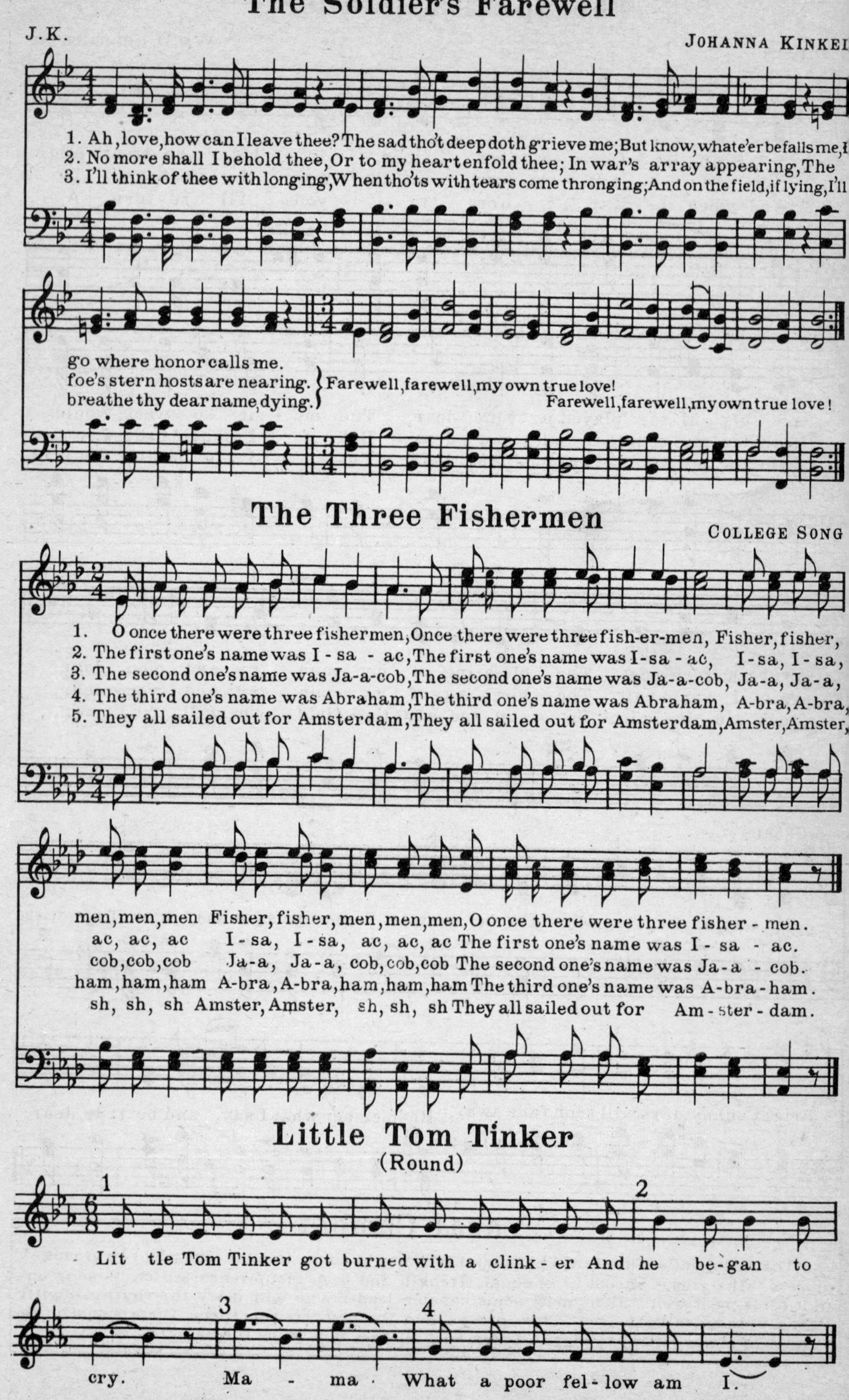
The Soldier's Farewell
J.K.
JOHANNA KINKEL
1. Ah, love, how can I leave thee? The sad tho't deep doth grieve me; But know, whate'er befalls me, I go where honor calls me.
2. No more shall I behold thee, Or to my heart enfold thee; In war's array appearing, The foe's stern hosts are nearing.
3. I'll think of thee with longing, When tho'ts with tears come thronging; And on the field, if lying, I'll breathe thy dear name, dying.
Farewell, farewell, my own true love!
Farewell, farewell, my own true love!
The Three Fishermen
COLLEGE SONG
1. O once there were three fishermen, Once there were three fish-er-men, Fisher, fisher, men, men, men Fisher, fisher, men, men, men, O once there were three fisher - men.
2. The first one's name was I - sa - ac, The first one's name was I-sa - ac, I - sa, I - sa, ac, ac, ac I - sa, I - sa, ac, ac, ac The first one's name was I - sa - ac.
3. The second one's name was Ja-a-cob, The second one's name was Ja-a-cob, Ja-a, Ja-a, cob, cob, cob Ja-a, Ja-a, cob, cob, cob The second one's name was Ja-a - cob.
4. The third one's name was Abraham, The third one's name was Abraham, A-bra, A-bra, ham, ham, ham A-bra, A-bra, ham, ham, ham The third one's name was A-bra-ham.
5. They all sailed out for Amsterdam, They all sailed out for Amsterdam, Amster, Amster, sh, sh, sh Amster, Amster, sh, sh, sh They all sailed out for Am - ster - dam.
Little Tom Tinker
(Round)
1 Lit tle Tom Tinker got burned with a clink - er And he 2 be-gan to cry. 3 Ma - ma 4 What a poor fel - low am I.

Gaily The Troubadour
T. H. B.
THOMAS H. BAYLY
1. Gai-ly the Troubadour touch'd his guitar, When he was hast'ening home from the war.
2. She for the Troubadour hopelessly wept; Sad-ly she thot of him when others slept.
3. Hark 'twas the Troubadour breathing her name, Under the battlement softly he came;
Singing: "From Pales-tine hith-er I come, La-dy love, la-dy love, welcome me home!"
Singing: "In search of thee would I might roam, Troubadour, Troubadour, come to thy home!"
Singing: "From Pales-tine hith-er I come, La-dy love, la-dy love, welcome me home!"
The Quilting Party
COLLEGE SONG
In the sky the bright stars glit-tered, On the bank the pale moon shone;
Fine.
And 'twas from Aunt Di-nah's quilt-ing par-ty I was see-ing Nel-lie home.
CHORUS
D.S. al Fine
I was see-ing Nel-lie home, I was see-ing Nel-lie home;
Merrily, Merrily
(Round)
1
2
Mer-ri-ly, mer-ri-ly, greet the morn; Cheer-i-ly, cheer-i-ly sound the horn.
3
4
Hark! to the ech-oes, hear them play O'er hill and dale, far, far, a-way.

"Stunt" Songs

The Golden Book of Favorite Songs will be found invaluable for use at banquets, community meetings and other adult gatherings. For such occasions, a short time devoted to singing will do more to unify the people and bring them into a neighborly and co-operative spirit than anything else possible. Have an adequate supply of books and secure a competent leader of singing. This leader need not be a great musician but must possess qualities of leadership and a strong sense of rhythm. In addition to patriotic songs and the old songs known and loved universally, a few good "stunt" numbers are in order. Several of these follow together with some standard popular numbers.

Welcome, Neighbor

Hello Speaker

(Tune for following is first phrase of Twinkle, Twinkle Little Star, page 84.)

Welcome, neighbor, how do you do?
We're mighty glad to meet with you.

Hello, speaker, we're your friend,
We'll stay with you until the end

Hail, Hail

(Key of G)

Hail, hail, the gang's all here,
Never mind the weather,
Here we are together
Hail, hail, the gang's all here
Let the trouble start RIGHT NOW.

O Me! O My! (A Toast)

(Substitute any name for the words "the speaker")

O me! O my! We'll get there by and by. If anybody likes the speaker, It's I, I, I, I, I.
O my! O me! We're hap-py as can be. If anybody likes the speaker, It's me, me, me, me, me

How D'ye Do

(This number may be used at banquets by having various tables compete with one another in improvising words to suit the melody. Any name may be substituted for "Mister Johnson.")

How d'ye do, Mister Johnson? How d'ye do? Is there anything that we can do for you?

We will do it if we can, We'll stand by you to a man. How d'ye do, Mister Johnson? How d'ye do, do, do

MacDonald's Farm

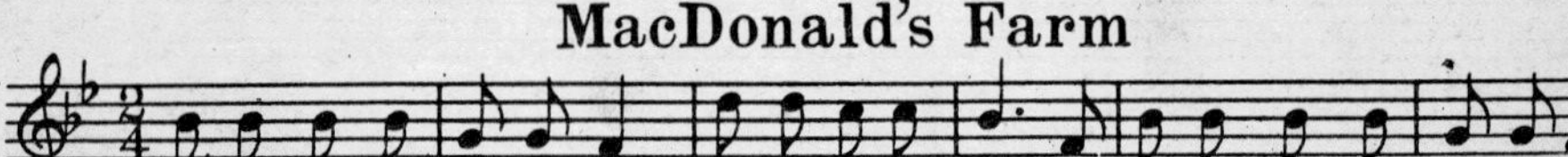
Old MacDonald had a farm, Ee-i, ee-i-o, And on this farm he had a duck

Ee-i, ee-i-o, With a quack, quack here and a quack, quack there, Here a quack, there a qua

Here and there a quack, quack, Old MacDonald had a farm, Ee-i-ee-i-o.

Continue indefinitely by using names and sounds of other animals. Do not overlook the Ford, with its "rattle," as a necessary farm adjunct.

The Mummy Song

(Tune—"The Long, Long Trail"—Key of G)

It's a short, short life we live here
So let us give while we may
And a song for every moment
Of the whole bright day.

What's the use of looking gloomy,
Or what's the use of our tears,
When we know a Mummy's had no fun
For more'n Three-Thousand Years.

The Tree In The Wood

NGLISH FOLK SONG
1. All in a wood there grew a tree, The fin-est tree you ev-er did see,
2. And on this tree there grew a limb, The fin-est limb you
And the green leaves grew a-round, a-round, a-round, And the green leaves grew a-round.
ever did see; The limb was on the tree, The tree was in the wood,
And the green leaves grew a-round, around, around, And the green leaves grew a round.
. Branch. 4. Nest. 5. Egg. 6. Yolk. 7. Bird. 8. Wing. 9. Feather.

As each item is added in successive verses, the preceding items are repeated in reverse order. Thus the last verse would run as follows:

And on the wing there was a feather,
The finest feather you ever did see,
The feather was on the wing,
The wing was on the bird,
The bird was in the yolk,
The yolk was in the egg,
The egg was in the nest,
The nest was on the branch,
The branch was on the limb,
The limb was on the tree,
The tree was in the wood,
And the green leaves grew around, around, around,
And the green leaves grew around.

Ham and Eggs

(Tune—Tammany—Key of D)

Leader: Ham and Eggs.
Echo: Ham and Eggs.
L: I like mine fried good and brown.
E: I like mine fried upside down.
L: Ham and Eggs.
E: Ham and Eggs.
L: Flip 'em.
E: Flop 'em.
L: Flip 'em.
E: Flop 'em.
All: Ham and Eggs.

A Laugh Provoker

(Tune—Battle Hymn of the Republic)
For music see page 12.

It isn't any trouble just to s-m-i-l-e.
It isn't any trouble just to s-m-i-l-e.
So smile when you're in trouble,
It will vanish like a bubble,
If you'll only take the trouble
Just to s-m-i-l-e.

SECOND VERSE L-a-u-g-h
THIRD VERSE G-r-i-n. Grin
FOURTH VERSE Ha, ha, ha, ha, ha

Alouette

FRENCH CANADIAN FOLK SON[G]

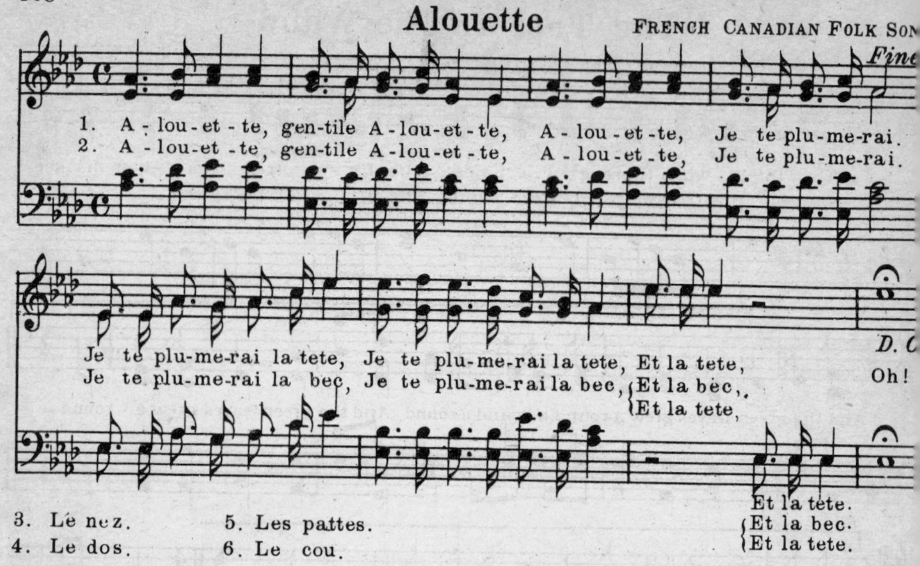
Fine
1. A - lou - et - te, gen-tile A - lou - et - te, A - lou - et - te, Je te plu - me - rai.
2. A - lou - et - te, gen-tile A - lou - et - te, A - lou - et - te, Je te plu - me - rai.
Je te plu-me-rai la tete, Je te plu-me-rai la tete, Et la tete,
Je te plu-me-rai la bec, Je te plu-me-rai la bec, Et la bec, Et la tete,
D. C
Oh!
Et la tete.
Et la bec.
Et la tete.
3. Le nez.
4. Le dos.
5. Les pattes.
6. Le cou.

In the measure before the Oh! and the D.C. where the women's voices are echoed by the men's a word is added as each verse is sung and the words of preceding verses are sung in reverse order. Thus, in the last verse, the duet between women and men would run as follows: Et le cou, et le cou; et les pattes, et les pattes; et le dos, et le dos; et le nez, et le nez; et la bec, e[t] la bec; et la tete, et la tete; Oh! and then back to the beginning to the Fine.

A Gymnastic Relief

(*Key of A flat*)

After or during a long speaking program
TUNE—Till We Meet Again

Smile awhile and give your face a rest,
(All smile)
Stretch awhile and ease your manly chest,
(Arms to side)
Reach your hands up toward the sky,
(Hands up)
While you watch them with your eye.
(Heads up)
Jump awhile, and shake a leg there sir!
(Jump lively)
Now step forward, backward—as you were.
(Step back and forth)
Then reach right out to someone near,
(Shake hands with neighbor)
Shake his hand and smile.
(All smile)

The Long Trail

(*Key of A flat*)

Copyrighted by M. Witmark & Sons and used by permission

There's a long, long trail a-winding
Into the land of my dreams,
Where the nightingales are singing
And a white moon beams.
There's a long, long night of waiting
Until my dreams all come true,
Till the day when I'll be going
Down that long, long trail with you.

Smiles

(*Key of A flat*)

Copyrighted by Jerome H. Remick and Company and used by permission

There are smiles that make us happy,
There are smiles that make us blue,
There are smiles that steal away the teardrops,
As the sunbeams steal away the dew.
There are smiles that have a tender meaning
That the eyes of love alone may see,
But the smiles that fill my life with sunshine,
Are the smiles that you give to me.

Perfect Day

(*Key of A flat*)

Copyrighted by Carrie Jacobs Bond and used by permission

When you come to the end of a perfect day,
And you sit alone with your thoughts
While the chimes ring out with a carol gay
For the joy that the day has brought;
Do you think what the end of a perfect day
Can mean to a tired heart?
When the sun goes down with a flaming ray
And the dear friends have to part.

Well this is the end of a perfect day,
Near the end of a journey too;
But it leaves a thought that is big and strong,
With a wish that is kind and true.
For memory has painted this perfect day
In colors that never fade,
And we find at the end of a perfect day
The soul of a friend we've made.